DETROIT PUBLIC LIBRARY
3 5674 00918685 0

D1156770

SIR WALTER RALEIGH

Captain & Adventurer

by Geoffrey Trease

THE VANGUARD PRESS, INC.

NEW YORK

Designed by Marshall Lee
Manufactured in the United States of America
by H. Wolff, New York, N. Y.

for Jill

Contents

Sir Walter Raleigh

CHAPTER I

The Devon Boy

THE HOUSE was long, built of gray stone, with several gables rising to break the golden expanse of thatched roof. It is still there, for that matter, as little changed as a house can be, if you remember that it is four centuries since Walter Raleigh was born.

It was not large, but it was a gentleman's house. Mr. Raleigh moved there from another manor on the edge of Dartmoor. This new home, Hayes Barton, never belonged to him—he leased it from some people named Duke. Many years later Walter wrote to them, begging them to sell him the house in which he had been born and spent so happy a childhood, but they would not. The place had suited his father, because he owned land at Withycombe Raleigh and Colaton Raleigh, and Hayes Barton was midway between.

The house was built like a capital E, facing south

to the English Channel, three miles away, though you had to walk up the sloping fields to get the view. The middle arm of the E was formed by the porch, which stuck out to shelter the door, heavy, black, and iron studded. Just inside was the winding staircase, tricky when you were small.

Walter was born in the large bedroom which occupied the whole upper floor of the west wing—the third arm of the letter E. But most of his early childhood memories were of the kitchen, which was also the main living room for the family, downstairs in the east wing.

That was the place for life and bustle, where the maids scurried about under his mother's eye, baking and basting and broiling immense meals over heaped-up fires of logs and peat. That was where the whole family, servants included, sat down to dinner at the long trestle table, and where on winter nights they clustered around to sing carols and madrigals, to roast chestnuts and heat their ale with spices, and to tell tales of ghosts, witches, and adventure beyond the sea.

Walter listened, wonder holding open his sleep-heavy eyes. What adventures they had had, these uncles and cousins of his! Some day he would grow up and have adventures, too, not stay at home like Father. Some day . . . some day . . .

He yawned, rocking on his low stool, more than halfway across the frontier between sleep and waking, dream and reality.

If only the family could have seen into the future at that moment and known even a quarter of what destiny had in store for young Walter, it would have been *their* eyes that opened wider, *their* yarns that died unspun upon their bearded lips.

Almost his first memory was of the news arriving that Queen Mary was dead, and that the Protestant girl, Elizabeth, had succeeded to the throne. That was in 1558. He was six, old enough to put off the little coats of babyhood and be breeched. It was quite a ceremony, with the tailor out from Exeter and all the household standing around with pins and laces and jokes and advice. Walter could not have been more fussed over if he had been a bride. The suit was just like a man's in miniature–there was even a sword for full-dress occasions.

"There," said the tailor. "How's that, Mrs. Raleigh? Quite the little gentleman, don't you think?"

Of course he was a gentleman, thought Walter. That was the one fact which had always been impressed upon him. He might live in a small house, little more than a farm, but he was the son of Walter Raleigh, Esquire, and related to half the best families in Devon.

There was a reason why he had so many relatives. Father had married three times, so Walter started with a large selection of half-brothers and half-sisters older than himself. Then Mother had been married before, and brought three boys of her own—John, Humphrey, and Adrian Gilbert—to make matters still more complicated. Walter had one full brother, Carew, two years older than himself.

Mother had been Katharine Champernoun originally; Uncle Arthur Champernoun, her brother, held the command at Plymouth as Vice-Admiral of the West—that important post was kept in the family for fifty years on end. Everyone (except Father) went to sea. It seemed to be in the blood.

Now he was old enough to run about on his own, Walter spent a lot of time on the beach. There was a fishing village where the little River Otter ran into the sea—it was called Salterton, because salt was got there by evaporating sea water in pans. There were salmon and sea trout in the river, mackerel and pilchards in the sea. Walter learned how to carry them as the fisherboys did, by forcing his finger through their gills and out of their mouths. Big boys, with long

younger who were excited about ideas and talked continually about them. There was Philip Sidney, next door at Christ Church—brilliant young aristocrat, son of the Lord-Deputy of Ireland, with enough charm and brains to take him anywhere. But, like Walter, Philip had so many different interests no one could be sure where he *would* end. When he showed you his poems, you felt that must be his line, to be England's first great sonnet writer, and a few years later you felt you had been right when you read:

> *With how sad steps, O moon, thou climb'st*
> *the skies!*
> *How silently, and with how wan a face!*

Yet when Philip started talking politics, with his pet scheme for a grand alliance of Protestant nations, you knew he was destined for glory as a statesman.

What none of you guessed was that he would die of a Spanish bullet at the siege of Zutphen before he was thirty-five, and be remembered chiefly for his chivalry in giving his cup of water to another wounded man.

Philip was only one, though perhaps the most outstanding. There was Dick Hakluyt, also at Christ Church, with his passion for tales of travel beyond the seas. He collected such tales as another boy might have collected butterflies. He and Walter found plenty to talk about. In later years Dick collected all those stories and records into his many-volumed book of *Voyages*, and Walter helped him, contributing his own *Discovery of Guiana* to the work.

Then there was John Lyly, always grumbling wittily that Oxford was a sheer waste of time, yet stopping his full three years, taking his degree, and even going on to Cambridge later for another. He was interested, above all, in books and writing, and argued that the style of your writing mattered much more than what you had to say. He was destined to become the first English novelist and to invent an affected, fanciful style which became very fashionable. Walter was amused by it, but he did not admire it. He preferred plain English.

Of the boys who were up at Oxford with Walter these three were perhaps the most famous in after-days, but there were many others, like the poor scholar Dick Hooker, a tradesman's son from near Exeter, who afterward became Master of the Temple and, with the many learned volumes he wrote, an outstanding champion of the Church. If Walter was "the ornament of the juniors," he must have had a good brain indeed.

What did they talk about? Rather ask, what did they not talk about?

Politics . . . Would the young Queen marry? If so, whom? Should England take her lead from Spain, or dared we defy the strongest country in Europe? Was it fair that all the newly discovered lands in the world should be divided between Spain and Portugal, as the Pope had said? Why should there be nothing left for England?

Science . . . Was it true that you could make gold by chemical experiment? Was the hour of a man's death fixed by the position of the planets at the moment of his birth?

Religion, books, plays . . . fashions in clothes (for the gentleman must pay as much attention to them as the lady). . . . They discussed everything.

And most of all they talked about themselves, what they would be and what they would do.

Walter never made friends easily. He was proud, he knew his own value and showed that he knew it, and he had a sharp tongue which sometimes gave more offense than he meant.

A timid youth, who was a skillful archer, came to him one day. Another scholar had insulted him. He felt he ought to do something about it, but he was scared to fight.

"What ought I to do?" he asked Walter.

"Challenge him to a duel," said Walter promptly.

"A d-d-duel? B-but I—"

Walter looked at him with a cold smile. "With longbows," he said contemptuously, and walked away.

Tom Child, who was at Oriel with him, once lent him a gown. Walter forgot to return it, or did not trouble to; nor did he offer to pay for it. It was not a very serious matter, and probably hundreds of Oxford men have done the same down the centuries, but Tom Child remembered it and spoke of it years afterward.

That was one of Walter's faults, and it was to bring him trouble throughout his life. He had little tact; he did not stop to think how his words and actions would be taken by other people. He made enemies almost by accident, and enemies were the last thing he could afford to have.

Probably he would have got on better if he had been to school like the others and learned to mix more. Another reason why he seemed to many people proud and arrogant was that, in his own heart, he was not sure of himself and put on an outward show to hide it.

The son of Walter Raleigh, Esquire, had been somebody in his own corner of Devon; at Oxford he was nobody in particular. Even Uncle Arthur, Vice-Admiral of the West, meant nothing once you were out of the West Country.

Other boys had powerful friends who would help them on in their careers. Philip Sidney would go straight to Court when he left the University, and John Lyly could count on Sir William Cecil, the Queen's Secretary and the most powerful man in England, to push him forward.

Walter saw a choice in front of him.

He could go home to Devon and join some of his relatives in their seafaring ventures–go in with the Gilberts or the Carews or the Champernouns, make some money, perhaps in time get a knighthood and end his days as a respectable Devon gentleman, just one rung higher up the ladder than his father had been.

Or . . . what?

He could go out into the wider world, where the name of Raleigh was unknown–and make it known!

But how? That was the question. How to make a

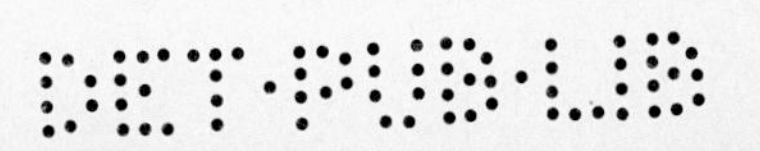

start, with no friends at Court, no money, only a good brain in a healthy young body to aid him?

Walter realized that the University alone would help him very little. It was easy enough to win distinction in the examination schools, but who noticed that? There was a sterner testing ground, the battlefield. But England was not at war.

That did not really matter very much, because an Englishman who wanted a fight could always find one. Walter had no difficulty.

Cousin Gawain Champernoun had married a French girl, Gabrielle de Montgomeri. Her father was one of the Huguenot leaders, waging civil war by fits and starts against the Catholic government in Paris. Though religion was made the excuse, it was, as usual, all mixed up with politics. The Huguenots, who were strongest in the southwestern quarter of France, were a middle-class party. Apart from their leader, the Prince of Condé, almost all the big nobles were on the other side. The Huguenots wanted France to be divided into several regions, each more or less governing itself, while the Catholics wanted a united country firmly directed from Paris.

Even without the family connection, Walter's sympathies would have been all on the Huguenot side, because they were Protestants and newly risen middle-class people like himself. So, when he heard that Cousin Gawain's brother Henry was thinking of going out to help with a troop of mounted volunteers from Devon, he decided to leave his books for the time being and go with them.

Cousin Henry, however, took his time. You could not gather a hundred suitable gentlemen, arm and horse them, and arrange transport all in five minutes. You had to go carefully, too. England was at peace with France. The Queen might disapprove of the expedition. Certainly, if it got into difficulties, she would not raise a finger to help it, for fear of giving offense in Paris.

"You remember what happened a few years ago?" one of Walter's friends asked him when he mentioned the plan.

"What do you mean?"

"That party of English volunteers who went out to join the Earl of Warwick when *he* was helping the Huguenots. Their boat went aground in enemy territory—the French hanged the lot of them, under a notice saying it was 'for having come, contrary to the wish of the Queen of England, to serve the Huguenots.' So, Walter, you know what to expect!"

Walter shrugged his shoulders. Naturally, if a man

wanted to do anything in the world he must take risks.

It looked as though Cousin Henry's expedition never would start. Patience was not one of Walter's virtues. When he got hold of an idea or made up his mind, he burned to act. He did not wait for Henry, but went.

He was still only a boy in his teens, but the French wars soon made a man of him. It was a bitter, savage struggle, as civil wars are apt to be, an affair of murders and massacres, with little to choose between the two sides. Both claimed to be fighting for true Christianity; both behaved as heathen savages would have been ashamed to.

Walter was in time for the Battle of Jarnac. Gaspard de Coligny, Admiral of France, was in command. He was the best of the Huguenot bunch, Walter found—a kindly, sensitive man, who would have been much happier reading or gardening but felt he must fight for his ideals. And in his case, at least, they were sincere.

Walter never forgot that day.

Coligny was leading the vanguard away from the banks of the River Charente. There was some muddle—some of the Huguenot gentlemen disobeyed orders, and the Duc d'Anjou made a surprise attack with his Catholic army. The Prince of Condé came galloping back to the rescue, and was killed. Walter saw defeat in all its horror.

It seemed that he had backed the losing side. Six months later he was with Count Louis of Nassau at the Battle of Moncontour, and it was the same tale again, defeat with heavy losses. Count Louis handled the retreat skillfully. As Walter wrote many years later, "Myself was an eyewitness, and was one of them that had cause to thank him for it."

Two days after the battle, Cousin Henry arrived at last with his hundred mounted volunteers from Devon. They carried a grim standard, showing a corpse with its head cut off, and the motto *Det mihi virtus finem*, "Let valor be my end."

Looking at it, Walter probably thought that Henry would live up to his motto better if he arrived more punctually for battles, but for once he did not say so. Henry's party had their bellyful of fighting before they finished, and not all of them saw Devon again. Their gloomy black flag proved sadly appropriate for the man they had come to help: when the Count de Montgomeri was forced to surrender a few years later, he was beheaded.

It was a horrible war. Walter came to the conclusion that civil war never did any country any good.

Yet he stayed on, fighting from time to time, probably because he did not know where else to go or what to do. He had won no glory, but at least he was learning one profession—soldiering. He stayed on, even after the ghastly Massacre of Saint Bartholomew had wiped out most of the Huguenot leaders, including Admiral Coligny. The beheading of his cousin's father-in-law seemed the end. He went back to England, not home, but to London.

What now? He entered himself as a law student at the Middle Temple, not because he had any intention of reading law—it made no appeal to his imagination and he ignored it whenever he could throughout his life—but because he knew the Queen thought highly of young men who had been through the Middle Temple and the other Inns of Court. She regarded such places as good training grounds for future statesmen.

Walter might know what he was doing, but no one could blame his family if they felt doubtful. The news which filtered down to them in Devon was not exactly encouraging.

He had moved out to Islington. . . . He was keeping strange company and playing wild pranks. . . . Two of his servants had been arrested for defying the watch. . . . He was seeing a good deal of his half-brother, Humphrey Gilbert, who was living in Limehouse and had done nothing definite for several years . . . and he was seeing far *too* much of George Gascoigne, a far older man with an unsavory record—had he not been in prison for gambling, lived wildly, and published scandalous writings?

What they did not realize at Hayes Barton (where gossip was out of date by the time it arrived) was that Gascoigne was now a reformed character. What appealed to Walter was not his wicked past but the originality of his mind. He wrote fluently in several forms, and whatever branch of literature he chose he was the first to try it. He wrote the first comedy in prose, the first masque, the first satire, and the first book on how to compose verses—besides being the first to translate an Italian tragedy into English.

Walter tried his own hand at verse from time to time—every gentleman did, but to Walter it was beginning to mean something more than mere scribbling. Not that he would ever devote his life to writing, of course; something in him craved for power and excitement. But when he wrote, he would write well.

He contributed some verses to Gascoigne's new book, *The Steel Glass.* Two lines were often remembered afterward—they might have been a bitter prophecy of his own life:

For whoso reaps renown above the rest
With heaps of hate shall surely be oppressed.

Humphrey's interests were utterly different. *His* mind was full of bold schemes for colonizing North America and finding a Northwest Passage by sea to China. He was not the only Englishman with that bee in his bonnet—Martin Frobisher was making yearly expeditions to find "the unknown goal," as men called it, declaring it "was the only thing in the world yet undone whereby a notable mind might be made famous and fortunate." Perhaps Frobisher exaggerated, but Walter and Humphrey agreed that, with the Spaniards in command of the Southwest Passage at Cape Horn and the Portuguese holding the Southeast Passage around the Cape of Good Hope, any man who found a Northwest Passage for England would be well rewarded.

But was there one? Humphrey had just published a book to prove there must be. All that was needed now was to go and find it.

Expeditions cost money. Never mind. Humphrey had an ingenious answer. Let the first move be to attack the Newfoundland fishing fleet—the fishermen were mostly Catholics and Spaniards, so there was no harm in that. The captured fishing boats could then be sold to the Dutch, the money used to build warships, and the warships used—to drive the Spaniards out of America. The continent could then be colonized by England, and it would be simplicity itself to find the Northwest Passage.

He wrote to the Queen's Privy Council about this enterprising scheme. They did not reply, but (as England was, after all, at peace with Spain) made half-hearted attempts to prevent his sailing. The authorities in Devon (who included Uncle Arthur at Plymouth) were ordered to stop him, but somehow they failed. Possibly because they included Uncle Arthur.

Walter went too, commanding a little ship called the *Falcon*, with the brave but sensible motto, *Nec mortem peto nec finem fugio*, "I neither seek death nor flee the end."

They did not worry unduly at Hayes Barton when they heard that Walter had gone with John and Humphrey on a voyage forbidden by the government. Devon men were always doing that. So long as they apologized afterward—and so long as they succeeded in their venture—nobody was very angry, except the Spaniards. The young man was better at sea than in London, where he was always in trouble, it seemed.

Soon they had more cause to worry, as the other ships came straggling home with tales of bad weather, desertion, and disaster. Had Walter gone down with the *Falcon*, or had he been taken by the Spaniards?

At last the good news came that his ship was safe in Plymouth Sound, and that he was alive, though he had been nearly killed in a fight with the Spaniards, who had inflicted heavy losses on his crew. Even so, he had given up only because of the weather and lack of provisions. On landing he had gone straight to the Mayor of Plymouth and laid a charge of desertion against one of his companions, Knollys, a relative of the Queen.

His mother sighed at that last item of news. Poor Walter! Would the boy never learn any tact? Now he would be wondering why he never seemed to get on in the world!

CHAPTER III

The Lost Land

"THIS YEAR I am twenty-eight," Walter reflected gloomily, "and what have I done?"

He seemed no nearer the Court than he had been at eighteen. He had tried soldiering in France, and he had been to sea. He had better go to Ireland next.

There was always work for an Englishman there, especially a Devon man. It was a great, half-empty island, soft and green as his own West Country, a fine place for horses and cattle, only needing English gentlemen to organize it.

Unfortunately, it was inhabited by ragged, half-starved Irishmen who could not understand the blessings of English government and preferred to keep their freedom. Traitors all, from their cradles! Walter knew just how they should be treated.

Not that he had ever yet put foot on the island, but he had heard plenty about it from his boyhood. It was one of his relatives, Sir Peter Carew, who had first gone to Munster twelve years before and ravaged that lovely southwestern corner of the country, where the Kerry Mountains roll dark against the west, and the Killarney lakes spread like blue satin under the summer skies.

"I stood no nonsense," Sir Peter had told the family. "Anyone who belonged to an outlaw band—anyone who sheltered them or gave them food—death! Like that. They treat us the same if they get the chance. Luckily they haven't much in the way of arms. Little throwing spears, and so forth."

Several dozen gentlemen of Devon had followed him out to Munster. Humphrey Gilbert had been one—he had served as president of the colony. That was how they saw Ireland, and made Walter see it: a wild, barbarous country, like America, only nearer, waiting for Englishmen to bring safe roads, law, order, and the Protestant religion.

After eleven years of these benefits, the ungrateful peasants were rising in revolt. All Munster was astir. The Earl of Desmond, timid and unwell, had been forced to undertake the leadership, yet it was an Englishman, strangely enough, who was pushing him forward—Nicholas Sanders, exiled Catholic, a man of great learning and magnetic character, whom the

Pope had sent to Ireland. With him were a Spaniard, Oviedo, also from Rome, and another Englishman, the Jesuit Father Allen.

The Irish felt they were fighting not only for their homes and their freedom, but also for their religion. It did not occur to them (as it did to the English) that they might also be fighting for Spain.

Desmond mounted his charger, lifting up a crucifix. His followers cheered and bellowed in Gaelic, "*Pápa Abú!*"—The Pope to victory!

Not only in Ireland, but in England and Spain, gentlemen reached for their swords.

In July, Walter received his commission from the Privy Council. He was given command of a hundred men newly conscripted in the City of London, with a first allotment of one hundred pounds for their pay. He himself was to draw four shillings a day, his men eightpence each, which was not bad money. Still, good pay was necessary. In other countries the soldier could hope for loot, but the Irish rebel was so poor that there was seldom anything worth removing from his cabin before you burned it. It was better, of course, for officers. They took their pickings in land, thousands of acres at a time.

They landed at Cork in August, and were in action a few weeks later. The situation was serious, and their arrival was most welcome.

A Spanish expedition, partly officered by Italians and flying the Pope's flag, had landed and occupied the old ruined fort of Smerwick, on the Kerry coast. On the way there they had captured a Bristol merchantman and thrown her crew into the sea to drown. Three hundred of them had marched inland to join the Earl of Desmond. The rest, seven hundred or so, were still in the fort. They had brought enough weapons to equip four thousand Irishmen.

Things looked ugly. Lord Grey, the English commander, was badly outnumbered. Once those four thousand rebels were armed, his forces would be swamped. It was a time for instant action, and no half measures.

Walter was one of the small column which hurried to Smerwick. As an experienced soldier he knew the danger, and for personal reasons he was eager to meet the enemy. One of his cousins had been killed in a rebel ambush a week or two before, and another had just escaped with his life.

They came to Smerwick, far out on the long mountainous promontory between Tralee Bay and Dingle Bay. Brandon Hill rose majestically behind them, over three thousand feet high. In front lay the

Atlantic, purple as a plum, with the islet of Great Blasket rising from the frothy breakers.

A bad place to be caught if the attack on the invaders failed. . . . Sea on three sides, and the only retreat a narrow passage between the ridge of Slieve Mish and the beach. . . . It could easily be blocked if the rebels rose behind them.

The attack must not fail.

There stood the stronghold of Dún-an-óir, the Fort of Gold, flying the Pope's banner together with ensigns of black and white. An Italian, San Joseph, was in command, and the garrison was mixed—Spanish Basques, Irishmen, and Italian brigands whom Gregory XIII had pardoned on condition they enlisted. Dr. Sanders and one or two other English Catholics were also inside.

There was a little skirmishing and bombardment, without much damage to either party. The matter was really settled when the squadron of Admiral Fitzwilliam Winter appeared in sight and the foreigners knew themselves cut off by sea. In spite of Dr. Sanders and the Irishmen, they insisted on running up the white flag.

Lord Grey refused conditions of surrender. The invaders had sailed with the approval of the Spanish king, but they did not carry his commission and were not entitled to be treated as prisoners of war. They were pirates, he argued, and decided to treat them as such. In any case, he could spare no men to guard them if they lived: he had still the main body of Desmond's rebels to deal with.

Only the captured officers were set aside for ransom. Walter and another officer, Captain Mackworth (who was murdered later by the O'Connors), were ordered to take their men into the courtyard and slaughter the rank and file as they stood beside their stacked weapons.

It was a horrible business. But Walter was hardened by similar scenes he had witnessed in France. He remembered his cousin and the crew of the Bristol trader. He obeyed the order. Everyone seemed to think it was the only thing to do.

It was thought that Dr. Sanders had perished in the massacre. But he was seen alive some time afterward at the Battle of Gort-na-Tibrid, when the rebels defeated the English with a loss of three hundred men. A little later the man who had once lectured in the quiet halls of Oxford and Louvain died of hunger at the foot of a lonely tree in the wilds of Kerry.

Walter believed in harsh methods in Ireland—he argued that it was "kill or be killed"—but he did not pretend to enjoy the campaign.

Ireland was a lovely country of green hills and blue water, mauve bog and silver birch, but he could hardly appreciate that when his eyes were blinded with smoke and blood.

The English columns rode to and fro in Munster. They checked on one another's whereabouts by the glare of burning villages, pinpointing the rocky coast in the darkness. They saw men, women, and children dying by inches from starvation. In many places people had nothing to eat but herbs, berries, and cress from the streams.

It was all very well to say that this lush countryside could have been another Devon, running with cider and cream, if it were colonized by Devon men. How could it be done, short of murdering every single Irishman?

It was a lost land, he told a friend, "a commonwealth of woe."

Meanwhile he was a soldier, with work to do.

On one occasion he was riding from Youghal to Cork with only seven or eight men. It was dangerous country, where one of the guerrilla leaders, the Seneschal of Imokillie, was known to be on the warpath.

Walter rode in front with his guide and one of his men, Harry Moile, while the rest were some way behind.

They came to a ford over the Ballinacurra River and were splashing through when there was a blood-curdling chorus of yells, and twenty or thirty rebels burst from the bushes. Walter ducked over his horse's mane and spurred forward. He was safely across when there was a shout for help from Moile, and, turning in his saddle, he saw that the man had been thrown and was struggling in midstream. The rebels rushed triumphantly into the shallows.

Walter turned. "All right!" he shouted. "I'm coming."

He plunged back, twirling an iron-shod quarter-staff. The Irishmen wavered before his furious charge. Moile was all right, he was wading ashore, but the horse had been seized by the enemy; the rest of the party were galloping hard for the ford. Walter plucked out a pistol and held it with the reins in his left hand, while with the other he grasped the quarterstaff.

"Come on!" he invited his attackers, but they preferred to go.

A few days later, at a parley with the Seneschal,

Walter challenged him to single combat, but the Seneschal, like his men, preferred not to accept.

Walter was winning a reputation for bravery. Colonel Zouch, who was commanding in Munster, chose him for a special mission.

"We're worried about Lord Roche," he explained. "He's *supposed* to be loyal, but you can't be sure of anyone in this country. We want him arrested and brought to Cork."

"Very good, sir."

"I warn you, it won't be an easy thing. He's shut himself up in his castle—that's a good twenty miles from here, rough marching, through the heart of the Seneschal's country. I can't give you more than a hundred men."

"Leave him to me, sir."

Walter took ninety men, left the city by the North Gate under cover of dark, and arrived at the castle, after a grueling forced march, before daybreak. There was just time to post his men in close cover around the gate before the growing light revealed them to the sentries.

He himself marched boldly up to the entrance with only six men behind him. Instantly there was a great stir within. The walls were lined with inquisitive faces, and he saw rows of ugly-looking boulders poised on the battlements to discourage uninvited guests.

"What do you want?" a voice demanded.

"My business is with his lordship. Can't I come in? Surely you're not afraid?"

There was a short pause while a message was taken to Roche, and very soon the answer came back: would Captain Raleigh breakfast with his lordship? Walter accepted gratefully. He was allowed to enter, but with only three of his followers.

He walked in, his brain cool but busy. He was taking his life in his hands. If anything went wrong, this breakfast would be his last meal. Long before dinnertime he would be hanging from the battlements.

Lord Roche proved to be a most pleasant gentleman, and his breakfast table was well laden. Walter found the meal extremely welcome after the long night journey. He only wished his men were faring as well.

"Now what can I do for you, Captain Raleigh?" said his host.

"I have orders, my lord, to escort you and Lady Roche to Cork."

The Irishman smiled. "And suppose I don't want to go?"

Walter shrugged his shoulders. "I have to persuade you, my lord."

"Look here, my dear fellow, do you know how many of my tenants are now gathered in this castle—men who'd die for me, if need be? Five hundred!"

"In that case I can't imagine why your gatekeeper was afraid to let the rest of my small party inside."

"Afraid?" Lord Roche flushed slightly and laughed. Then, turning in his chair, he gave instructions, "Let the rest of Captain Raleigh's party come inside. Yes, that's an order. Why should *they* go without breakfast?"

Would it work? Walter continued eating and talking, but from time to time his eyes strayed to the far end of the hall. At last came the signal he was waiting for. All his men were inside the castle, the whole ninety, picked men who knew just what to do.

"I think, my lord," he said quietly, "you had better change your mind and come with me to Cork."

"Eh? What—?" Lord Roche found himself gazing into the muzzle of a pistol. "Captain Raleigh, this is an outrage!"

"So is rebellion against the Queen."

His host recovered himself. "You surely don't imagine, my dear fellow, that you can get out of here alive?"

"I have more men with me than perhaps you imagined, my lord. Thank you for letting them in."

"My tenants will tear you limb from limb—"

"Not if they know that the slightest attempt to interfere will mean that *you* die first."

Lord Roche was silent for a few moments while he thought it over. "You're a cunning devil, Captain Raleigh," he said at length. "Very well. I'll ride to Cork with you."

Walter would have been glad to leave at once, but his infantrymen could not face that twenty miles back without food and rest. By the time they were ready to move, the countryside would be in arms against them. While they were about it they might as well wait for the cover of darkness again.

It was an uncomfortable day. Conversation with his host was awkward, to say the least. Finally, at midnight, his column was ready to move off.

The night was wild. The rain came down as only Irish rain can. Yet it probably saved their lives, for the Seneschal of Imokillie was out with eight hundred men to catch them on their way back. The two forces missed each other in the storm.

The march was bad enough without any fighting.

Men set their teeth, bowed their heads, and plodded on. One man dropped and died, but at dawn they were marching through the city gate amid the cheers of their comrades.

Walter was glad that nothing unpleasant happened to Lord Roche in the end. It had, after all, been a very good breakfast.

That December he returned to England, carrying dispatches from Colonel Zouch to the Privy Council. If he made a good impression upon them, he would be given an audience with the Queen. His big chance had come at last.

CHAPTER IV

At the Court of the Queen

HE HAD SEEN Elizabeth, spoken to her. . . . With a sudden happy inspiration he had won her smile and thanks.

They had all been walking through the palace garden when they came to a muddy patch across the path. Others had dithered. . . . "Take care, madam, your shoes . . ." It had been left to Walter to whip off his velvet cloak and spread it, with a magnificent gesture, to bridge the mud.

The cloak might never be the same again, but it had been worth it. The Queen might not remember the young officer with whom she had discussed Ireland, but she would not forget the man who had laid his cloak at her feet.

An amazing woman, he reflected. Poets sang of her beauty until their quills split with emotion; common sense reminded him she was almost fifty, neither a Greek goddess nor an English girl. Her cheeks were shrunken, the paint thick upon them. Her lips were too thin, her nose too high—and the fierce red of her hair was not natural.

She might lap up their flattery, but she *could* not believe it. She was no fool. Her questions about Ireland showed that. Her mind, tongue, eye were all alike, razor-sharp. She had ruled England for nearly twenty-five years and was now at the height of her powers.

That was the woman he had seen; what of the man *she* had seen? What impression would she have kept? Calmly, without conceit, he studied the long mirror and tried to guess.

At least he was tall. She would like that. And young, not yet thirty. Not bad looking, though no doubt his eyelids were too heavy and gave him a gloomy look. He had learned to carry himself like a soldier, and his clothes were finer than he could really afford. But it paid to dress splendidly. When he had money he would astonish them all.

Meantime, he had made a good start. She liked tall young men who dressed well and carried themselves with an air. That was important. No matter what your talents, if she did not fancy you, you might as well retire from public life.

Walter had no intention whatever of doing that.

The Queen paced her room, dictating letters to a secretary. "And this," she said, "to my Lord Deputy in Ireland."

"Yes, madam?"

"Our pleasure is to have our servant Walter Raleigh trained some time longer in that our realm for his better experience in martial affairs. . . ." She paused, thoughtful, her foot tapping the oaken floor. The pen squeaked over the paper.

She was not sure, after all, whether to send this young man back to Ireland and give him a company of infantry to command. He might be more useful in other ways.

In the end she changed her mind, as she so often did. Walter was sent with the Earl of Leicester's mission to Holland. She told him to make personal contact with the Prince of Orange. The Prince soon realized that this grave young man was trusted by the Queen. Her old favorite, the Earl of Leicester, was quietly slipping from his position. He would not last forever. Who would be next—this Raleigh? At all events he was a man to treat with respect.

So it was Walter who carried the Prince's dispatches back to England, and was charged with private messages for Her Majesty's ear alone.

"Tell her, *Sub umbra alarum tuarum protegimur*," said the Prince.

Under the shadow of thy wings are we protected. . . .

Very true, thought Walter. Protestant Holland seeks the sheltering wings of England against Spain. . . .

But the Latin tag would fit other cases, too. Poor but ambitious gentlemen must seek protection under royal wings. And that was his plan.

He never returned to Ireland except for short visits, and then not as an infantry captain. He was established now at Court. He set out to be the perfect courtier.

There was a book which laid down exactly what that meant, *The Courtier*, by an Italian named Castiglione, translated into English by Thomas Hoby twenty years before, and used ever since as a handbook for young men with hopes of promotion. Philip Sidney had all the qualities the book required; Walter had most of them. Physical courage, skill in arms, a cultured mind able to appreciate the arts and to toss off graceful poems when required, a knowledge of Greek and Latin, French and Spanish, good manners and appearance. . . . There was little Walter lacked but a title to his name.

He had studied another Italian book, Machiavelli's *Prince*. It was full of worldly wisdom about Court life and politics. He hated the ideas in it, even though he knew that they fitted the facts.

"*It must be evident to everyone*," said the book, "*that it is more praiseworthy for a prince always to maintain good faith, and practice integrity rather than craft and deceit. And yet the experience of our own times has shown that those princes have achieved great things who made small account of good faith. . . . A sagacious prince then cannot and should not fulfill his pledges when their observance is contrary to his interest. . . .*"

Like most Englishmen, Walter read Machiavelli, detested his advice—and, in spite of himself, learned from it a better understanding of the way in which kings and queens behaved. Few things angered him more than when enemies accused him, behind his back, of being an English Machiavelli himself.

He had enemies. It was impossible to be a courtier without. One man's success meant failure for somebody else. Court life was like a seesaw, and that could not be helped. But, as at Oxford, his manner made rather more enemies than he need have had.

The Queen liked him. She liked the soft Devon speech that his tongue never lost. She was fond of giving nicknames, so she called him "Water," suggesting (only half in fun) that like water he was unstable. That was hardly fair. Walter might be fond of dreams and schemes, but they were not wild ones. He stuck to them, and would put in any amount of hard, steady work to make them real.

Once, in those first months when he was feeling his way cautiously, he took a diamond and scribbled, as if idly, on the windowpane:

Fain would I climb, yet fear I to fall–

and the Queen, able to versify with any of her courtiers, grinned wickedly and wrote an answering line:

If thy heart fail thee, climb not at all.

That autumn, as she rode off to a staghunt, one of his rivals stepped from the woods and offered her a book, a bucket, and a jeweled bodkin or hairpin. Between the pages of the book she found a letter, complaining in poetic language that her faithful sheep were afraid of drowning. The Queen took in the meaning at once–she was quick at such code messages–and guessed the meaning of the bucket and the bodkin. If "Water" were not removed, his rival would stab himself.

"Don't be afraid," she promised with a twinkling eye, "my sheep are so dear to me I will see they take no harm from floods or—Water." And she rode on, chuckling, to the hunt.

In spite of her promise, "Water" continued to rise rapidly.

He needed money. He had to compete with men who came to Court with vast landed estates behind them, and could draw on the rents of a hundred farms to pay for their clothes and jewels and horses. He had nothing—yet.

The Queen seldom parted with money, never unless compelled. She had her own financial problems. But she gave her friends what could be turned into money without cost to herself.

She gave Walter estates in Ireland, taken from rebels. When he held as much as one man was allowed, he persuaded her to grant further land to men of his choosing, mere dummies who held it on his behalf. In this way he got possession of forty thousand acres in Munster.

She gave him a license to control the export of various cloths, and another for the sale of wines throughout England. This would have enabled him to collect a small fortune from the merchants concerned, but actually he had to let out his rights to an agent, and the income, though useful, was only moderate.

He must have a home worthy of his position. She let him live in Durham House, a mansion in the Strand which had once been the Bishop of Durham's. There plain Mr. Walter Raleigh lived with the greatest families in England for his neighbors. Somerset and Essex, Bedford and Arundel—every other house bore the name of a duke or an earl. He had forty servants to run the place, and as many horses in the stables.

From here he went forth to visit the Queen at Whitehall Palace, barely half a mile away. No peacock could have competed with Walter when he dressed up to conquer. Flowered doublet and hose of silver-white satin, exquisite lace at throat and wrist, rubies and pearls wherever they could be fixed—on hat and dagger hilt and velvet cape. One hatband of pearls was valued at eighty pounds. He had a pair of shoes worth more than six thousand gold pieces.

Such a man could not be ignored. But it certainly took money.

In one way Walter enjoyed this peacock-strutting—it satisfied one side of his nature—but the better part of him secretly despised it. He looked upon it as a means to an end.

He was far happier when he could slip away from the long banquets, the plays and masques, the dances that went on into the early hours of the morning, and snatch a few hours in the quiet of his study, set in a turret of Durham House, overlooking the Thames. There were his favorite books, his maps and globes. There he wrote poems. And there he talked with his true friends, speaking his thoughts freely and boldly, not wrapping them up in politeness and deceit, as one was forced to when conversing at Court.

Humphrey Gilbert came there, still set on his dream of the Northwest Passage. So did Thomas Hariot, mathematician, astronomer, and ablest scientist in England. Dick Hakluyt, his old Oxford friend, was a regular visitor, knowing that Walter's room was a clearinghouse for the travelers' tales which still fascinated him. There was Tom Cavendish, second Englishman to sail around the world, and Dr. John Dee, quaint astrologer and spiritualist, who was rumored to have dealings with the Devil.

Explorers, scientists, and writers were his favorite

company. These men were concerned with the truth of things. In the quest of truth they were fearless adventurers, risking their bodies at the ends of the earth or their souls on the frontiers of knowledge that men called forbidden.

Kit Marlowe, the brilliant young Cambridge poet, used to come there. He was just writing his first tragedy, *Tamerlane*, and hammering out blank verse such as no man had ever written before. Soon he was to follow it with his masterpiece, *Doctor Faustus*, the drama of the scientist who sacrificed everything, even his immortal soul, to gain new knowledge. Much of his inspiration came from men like Dee and Hariot, whom he had met in Walter's room.

Wonderful talks they had there—but it did not end only in talk. The dream which dominated Walter's whole life was gradually taking shape.

America . . .

Why should that immense new continent be Spanish, just because it had been discovered by a Spanish expedition—led, anyhow, by an Italian? Why should vast lands, as yet unseen and unnamed, be earmarked in advance for Spain and Portugal, merely because a Pope (whom England did not obey) decreed it should be so?

No. America, or some of it, should be English.

Ways must be found to make it so. He twirled the globe, laying his finger on the wide blanks of territory on which no European eye had ever rested.

The idea of the Northwest Passage was interesting and important—but he wanted to do something more than find a new route to China. Stories of gold and silver attracted some men, and he could use gold and silver himself—but he saw America as something more than a series of mines.

America was a place where Englishmen might live. He thought of the many ambitious gentlemen like himself, and of the thousands of country people who had lost their small holdings through the enclosure of land. Such folk had no employment left in England and were reduced to begging along the roads. Let them join with the gentlemen adventurers and carve new farms from the unknown continent.

Hardly anyone, as yet, had the imagination for such schemes. He had to begin with ideas they understood, or thought they understood.

First, he helped Sir Humphrey Gilbert to equip the voyage on which he was drowned. Walter spent two thousand pounds on fitting out a fine two-hundred-ton vessel, the *Bark Raleigh*, which fortunately returned safely. Walter enjoyed those preparations. From his boyhood days, when he carved skillful models and listened to the highly technical arguments of the local seamen, he had held his own decided views on ship design. Too many top-heavy ships were being built, he always considered—builders were so anxious to provide space for men and guns.

A year later he helped to organize a company called the Colleagues of the Discovery of the Northwest Passage. Humphrey's younger brother, Adrian, was in it. Even Dr. Dee, who was more interested in the spirits of the other world than in the trade routes of this, held shares. The Northwest Passage was not discovered, but a good deal of useful information was gained. Bit by bit the blank spaces on the map were being filled.

He had been at Court three years before he was able to take the next step and apply for the Queen's permission to found a colony in North America. It was given graciously, but on the clear understanding that "Water" himself should not run away. He was high in favor just then. She had knighted him, and a knighthood still meant something. But he knew that he dared not leave the Court, even if she allowed it. Once his back was turned his enemies would undermine his popularity by a sly word here and a cunning move there, more dangerous than the sapper's pick and gunpowder.

He sent out his main expedition in April, 1585. There were seven ships and three pinnaces, commanded by his cousin, Dick Grenville, a tough and brutal adventurer, later to win fame he hardly deserved by his death in the *Revenge*. Dick was merely to convey the expedition. Another Devon man, Ralph Lane, was to be governor of the colony. Young Tom Hariot, the scientific genius, went too.

In due course Dick came home, after enjoying a little piracy against the Spaniards on the way. He reported that the colonists had been comfortably landed, as arranged, on a small island off the American coast. He confirmed earlier accounts that the soil was fertile and the natives as "mannerly and civil as any of Europe."

Walter went on with his scheme hopefully and energetically. In the late winter he sent off a convoy with supplies for the colony, and waited eagerly for the news they would bring back. To his violent disappointment, the end of July brought very different news: a ship named the *Bark Bonner* had arrived in Plymouth, and all his colonists were aboard.

What on earth had happened? He could scarcely

wait until Lane and Hariot arrived in London with their story.

The winter had been severe and the Indians had turned hostile. While they were anxiously expecting the supply ships, Drake had called at the island and some of the more timid colonists had begged for a passage home. Drake had not encouraged them in this, but had offered them stores to tide them over until their own arrived. Then, unfortunately, he had lost some of his own transports in a storm and been forced to cut down his offer. This had merely depressed the colonists still more, and at the finish he had given them the *Bark Bonner* to bring them home. They had missed Walter's relief ships, as it turned out, by a couple of days.

"But you won't give up, will you?" urged Hariot. "It's a fine country. Not an earthly Paradise, of course, but excellent for colonization."

"No," said Walter, "we won't give up."

The place had to be named. When the first arrivals had asked the name of the country, the Indians had answered with the outlandish word "Wyngandacoia."

"But," Hariot explained with a chuckle, "that only means, in their language, 'How smartly dressed you are!' What they'd have said if *you'd* been with us, sir, I can't imagine."

"Wyngandacoia?" Walter made a face at the string of awkward syllables. "I know–let's name it Virginia, in honor of the Virgin Queen. That'll please Her Majesty."

"That's always very important," agreed Hariot with a smile.

He was an observant young man. Nothing escaped his eye, and Walter never ceased to be thankful that he had met him, seen his quality, and persuaded him into his service. Hariot had been with him before he reached the Court. He had come first, as a brilliant youth of twenty, to teach Walter the mathematics he needed for his ship designing, his navigation, and his other hobbies. He had stayed on as friend and faithful lieutenant.

He fascinated Walter now with his descriptions of the colony. People, plants, animals, minerals . . . he had noted everything. Where possible, he had brought back specimens, and these were now laid out in the study for all to examine. One which attracted particular attention was tobacco. Walter heard how the Indians smoked the dried and shredded leaves, sampled them himself, became a keen pipe smoker, and made the habit fashionable.

The Queen joked with him one day about it, and he solemnly assured her that he knew so much about tobacco he could even tell her the weight of the smoke.

"Rubbish, Water!" she retorted sharply.

"Will you wager against it, madam?"

"Of course." To bet on a certainty was her favorite form of commercial risk.

Walter called for scales, weighed a pipeful of tobacco, and began to smoke it. Then, without a smile, he tapped out the ash into the scalepan and weighed it.

"You will admit, madam, that the difference in weight must be the weight of the smoke?"

After a cautious moment, waiting to see how she would take it, everyone laughed. She took it well, though she disliked losing. "I've heard of many men who turned gold into smoke," she said tartly, "but Water's the first to turn smoke into gold!"

In the years that followed he sent out no fewer than seven expeditions, pouring out his own fortune on the scheme. Ill luck dogged him. His colonists disobeyed instructions, meddled in piracy, quarreled with the Indians . . . always there was something that went wrong.

"I shall yet live," he said between his teeth, "to see Virginia an English nation."

Meanwhile, in England, his star continued high and steady in the heavens.

He was one of the two Members of Parliament for Devon, speaking regularly and sensibly in the House of Commons. He followed Uncle Arthur as Vice-Admiral of the West. He was Lieutenant of Cornwall, and Lord Warden of the Stannaries. That last office made him head of the tin-mining industry, and lawgiver to twelve thousand rough West-countrymen. They held their court on Crockern Tor, high in the wild, misty wilderness of Dartmoor. There, on a granite throne, Walter administered mining law to men who cared little for the law of England.

Then came the honor which gave him most satisfaction of all: the Queen appointed him Captain of her Guard. It carried no pay, only (to quote the order):

"To our right trusty and well-beloved servant Sir Walter Raleigh, Knight, Captain of our Guard, six yards of tawny medley, at thirteen shillings and fourpence a yard; with a fur of black budge, rated at ten

pounds; sum, fourteen pounds; given to him for the office of Captain of our Guard."

A mere trifle to a man whose shoes were worth over six thousand gold pieces. But the post meant he was continually in personal attendance on the Queen. He could speak to her whenever he wished, and, standing on guard at the door of her Privy Chamber, he could not fail to hear most of what others said to her. If knowledge was power, she had given him more power than if she had made him commander of an army.

Walter ordered himself a suit of golden armor to wear in his new rank. The occasion deserved some form of celebration.

CHAPTER V

"The Spaniards Are Coming!"

A COURTIER could never afford to sit back and take things easily. It was an endless struggle to keep one's place in the Queen's favor.

Walter had no sooner mastered his new duties than a fresh rival appeared on the scene. The handsome nineteen-year-old Earl of Essex arrived, fresh from the siege of Zutphen, where Philip Sidney had been killed. The Queen took a fancy to him at once and made him Master of the Horse.

It was not long before Walter had trouble with him. They were both in attendance on the Queen when she paid a visit to the Earl of Warwick at North Hall, near London. They found Essex's sister staying there; as she was out of favor with the Queen, she was grimly warned to keep in her own room, out of the way. It was none of Walter's doing, but Essex chose to think so. He burst in upon the Queen as she was finishing her supper. Walter, on guard at the door, heard all that followed, as the young earl meant him to.

"It was done to please that knave Raleigh!" he stormed. He was an excitable youth and, whether in a temper or a fit of sulks, never hesitated to say what he liked to her. "You've disgraced me, you've disgraced my sister in the eyes of the whole world—merely to please Raleigh!"

Elizabeth would not have stood it from anyone else. Walter, stiff in the doorway, hand clenched on sword hilt, knew she would not have taken such words from him. But from this spoiled darling, her Robin, she would take anything, it seemed.

"You've no cause," she was saying, "to disdain Raleigh."

"Disdain!" the youth exploded. He proceeded to outline Walter's humble beginnings and more recent career, with some choice but unflattering comments on his general character. "Naturally I disdain a man like that. Do you think I consider him as my *competitor*? And do you think I can be happy serving a mistress who is in awe of such a person?"

He went on until the Queen could stand no more. She snubbed him quietly by turning away and speaking to the Countess of Warwick. Essex rushed out in a rage, shouting for his sister. Midnight though it was, he would not let her stay another minute in a house where she had been so insulted. She packed at once and set off for London.

Walter's anger was of another kind, cold and repressed. He could not challenge the Earl to a duel: he had been there only on duty as Captain of the Guard, officially deaf and blind to all that went on. Yet he could not swallow the insults that Essex had tossed over his shoulder. How could he retort?

He hit on a way. He wrote seven lines of ingenious verse. They would have meant nothing to any other reader, but the use of the word "disdain," echoing the Earl's own sneer, would tell the youth plainly what they signified and who had sent them. He arranged for someone to slip the paper into the Earl's pocket.

It was the only reply open to him at present. Sooner or later a proper reckoning would come. Meanwhile it at least relieved his feelings.

Soon there were more serious matters to occupy his mind. Philip of Spain was getting ready his Armada, to reconquer that island which once (as husband of Queen Mary) he had come to regard as a rightful possession of his own.

Walter served on the Council of War set up to

meet the danger. Alarming reports came in each week from merchants and secret agents on the Continent. Not only was Philip preparing great forces in Spain—he had others massing in the Spanish-held Netherlands, facing the Thames estuary across a narrow strip of sea. New galleons had been launched in the Dutch shipyards of the Scheldt. The Duke of Parma, who commanded there, had over two hundred landing barges, each big enough to hold thirty cavalry horses. The Pope, anxious to see England Catholic again, had promised Philip a million crowns as soon as the Spanish banner flew over an English beach.

Sir Francis Drake—bearded, curly headed, banging the council table with his fist, praying sincerely and loudly to God one minute and swearing frightfully the next—believed in meeting the Spaniards halfway, or, better still, before they even started. The Armada should be smashed in its own bases. If it were, the Duke of Parma's supporting expedition would never venture into the North Sea alone.

Walter supported Drake. But the Queen would have none of it. She feared to venture her precious ships. She inclined to the advice of her soldiers rather than her sailors: her fleet should be used to defend, not attack. They should form an outer defense line, backed by land batteries and troops. She saw them rather as floating fortresses than cavalry of the sea.

There it was. The Queen had her way. Walter made the best of it and labored unceasingly to make her policy effective. He rode thousands of miles, inspecting coast defenses from Land's End, in the west, to King's Lynn, on the Wash. His main efforts were spent on his own counties of Devon and Cornwall. There was his post so long as invasion threatened them.

The months passed. The beacons stood along the cliffs. His scattered little army, a few hundred horsemen, two thousand infantry or so, was ready to muster at the signal.

Meanwhile, Walter could find good company in Plymouth. Howard, the Lord High Admiral, was there with the *Ark Royal*, the ship which Walter had originally built as the *Ark Raleigh* a year before and sold to the Queen for five thousand pounds. It was of eight hundred tons, carrying four hundred men. Lord Howard said it was "the oddest ship in the world, and the best for all conditions."

Drake was there, flying his flag as Vice-Admiral of England in the *Revenge*. Frobisher was there, and John Hawkins, and many another famous captain. His half-brothers, John and Adrian Gilbert, were helping him with the defense of the southwest coast, and his cousin, Dick Grenville, was active in it too.

So the weeks passed, with rumors and false alarms, until the third week of July.

It was on a Friday, July the nineteenth, that Walter heard the news: the Armada, a mighty crescent of a hundred and twenty galleons and transports, advancing on a front of eight miles, had been sighted off the Lizard.

At last! The lonely cliff-top watchings were over; the weeks of idling in Plymouth, of yarning and drinking, of bowls and skittles, were ended. There was not a moment to be lost.

The very wind that was blowing the Spaniards on their way held the English fleet prisoner in the Sound. Somehow they must get the ships out into the open sea before the Armada arrived and bottled them up.

Walter had his own duties ashore, but his heart was with Howard and Drake. As he stood receiving reports and issuing instructions for the coast defenses, he watched with an agony of sympathy the frenzied efforts of his comrades to get their ships into the open Channel in the very teeth of the wind.

He saw the anchors weighed . . . saw the seamen in the boats straining at their long oars . . . saw the slack towropes slowly tauten and the bare-masted ships begin to glide slowly, ever so slowly, across the ruffled waters of the Sound.

Night fell. No one slept easily. It was hard to tell, from the lights bobbing in the darkness, how far the Admiral had succeeded. Only when day broke, drizzling and gray, could the watchers on the headlands see that most of the fleet were clear of the inlet. With sail spread now to the light breeze, they were standing out across the open Channel, groping to windward of the enemy.

And now for Walter, kept ashore by duty, the tiresome waiting began again.

"We'll see no action here," Adrian Gilbert was grumbling two days later. "Drake's bundling 'em up-Channel. They're past Dorset. They may try a landing in the Isle of Wight–I doubt it myself–but we certainly shan't see a Don in Devon."

"I hardly thought we should," said Walter. "With another fleet and army waiting to join them from the Netherlands, they'd be fools not to unite before they strike their blow."

"Drake's bundling 'em along all right," chuckled John Gilbert. "Seems, from the reports, he's trying to fold up their port wing onto their center—edge 'em closer and closer in, till they lack sea room for maneuver."

"The *San Salvador* has blown up," said Walter quietly. "Otherwise, so far, we haven't done much more than harass them, so far as I can see."

"And we not there," said Adrian dolefully.

Walter was silent for a moment. "Listen," he said. "You know it's as much as my head is worth to put to sea without the Queen's permission. But I'm sending my own *Roebuck* with ammunition for the fleet, and, if you want to go too, I'll take the responsibility of giving you permission."

They went rejoicing. With a sour smile Walter remained at his post.

After a day or two he got word to report in London. It was as clear there as it was to him that there would be no Spanish attack in the west. The Queen would employ him somewhere else—but he must await her decision.

The Armada was still sweeping majestically up the English Channel toward the Straits of Dover—and the meeting with the Duke of Parma. Dispatches reaching London told of a running fight, with fresh English vessels continually joining in from the south coast ports. Drake had captured a galleon, *Our Lady of the Rosary*, carrying wire whips for the flogging of English heretics and fifty thousand ducats in cash. Gossip said that Frobisher was furious with jealousy; if Drake did not give him a share of the prize, he swore, he "would have the best blood in his belly."

Meanwhile the Queen had driven down to Tilbury in her coach to join the army of sixteen thousand men waiting for the attack on the Thames mouth, which now seemed more and more likely as the Armada drew nearer to its meeting with the Duke of Parma.

Essex was down there with his own little contingent of two hundred light cavalry, sixty musketeers, and sixty arquebusiers, all very tastefully uniformed in orange with facings of white silk. He must have been near, thought Walter enviously, when the Queen rode through the ranks, fearless of assassins, a gallant figure on a great white horse. . . . How like her to put on a steel breastplate, to have her helmet carried before her by a page, yet—woman still—to put on her jewels for the occasion! And how like her, those words that were already ringing through England, that she had spoken to the parade!

"My loving people, we have been persuaded by some that are careful of our safety to take heed how we commit ourselves to armed multitudes, for fear of treachery. But I assure you I do not desire to live to distrust my faithful and loving people. Let tyrants fear! *I* have always so behaved myself that, under God, I have placed my chiefest strength and safeguard in the loyal hearts and good will of my subjects.

"I am come amongst you at this time not for my recreation and disport but being resolved, in the midst and heat of the battle, to live and die amongst you all, to lay down for my God, and for my kingdom, and for my people, my honor and my blood, even in the dust.

"I know I have but the body of a weak and feeble woman, but I have the heart and stomach of a king, and a king of England, too, and think foul scorn that Parma or Spain or any prince of Europe should dare to invade the borders of my realm. To which, rather than any dishonor shall grow by me, I myself will take up arms, I myself will be your general, judge and rewarder of every one of your virtues in the field!"

Yes, Essex had been there, standing close, hearing the words as they fell from the proud curve of her lips.

And he, Walter Raleigh, had to kick his heels

among the clerks and secretaries in London, awaiting orders.

Drake had certainly had the best of the running fight up-Channel, but the danger to England was now greater rather than less. The Duke of Medina Sidonia had lost some ships, but he had brought the bulk of the Armada safely to the Straits of Dover. He was now lying at the fortified seaport of Gravelines, midway between Dunkirk and Calais, waiting for the Duke of Parma to embark his invasion army from the Netherlands. It was clear that the Spaniards had succeeded in the first stage of their plan.

Suddenly a courier from Tilbury brought Walter his orders. Together with Richard Drake he was to join the fleet at once, with all speed. He was to carry the Queen's instructions to the Lord High Admiral: attack the Armada in some way or burn it.

They took to horse, crossed London Bridge and broke into a gallop as the Kentish road opened before them. . . .

"Or burn it."

The Queen's own words had suggested a way to drive the Armada from its sheltered anchorage. At the hastily summoned Council of War aboard the *Ark Royal* it was decided to send fireships against the galleons that very night. There would be a flood tide racing up the Channel, and the breeze would be right if it held in its present quarter; tide and breeze together would carry ships straight into the anchorage without need of human hand to steer.

Preparations were hastily made. There was no time to bring worthless hulks from Dover; eight of the smaller, less seaworthy English vessels must be sacrificed. They were got ready under cover of the other ships.

Decks, masts, even sails were daubed with brimstone, pitch, resin—whatever would burn. Even the cannon were fully charged. They would fire themselves when the heat reached the powder.

Night gathered. There had been rain, there was no moon, and scarcely a star winked overhead. Nothing showed in the darkness but the lanterns of the two anchored fleets, their reflections shifting slightly, like golden chains, in the black water lapping under their sides.

Walter waited, with the others, impatient for the turn of the tide. It was midnight. . . . Not long now, perhaps half an hour . . . Yes, the slack water was turning to one of those racing tides which Drake knew so well from his boyhood experience of Dover Straits, and now—yes, look!—a sheet of flame, a ruby glow outlining every mast and spar of the vessels between! The fireships had been cast off, wind and tide were sweeping them into the Spanish anchorage!

It was a wild hour. They could hear the peal of Spanish trumpets, the drums beating to quarters. . . . The eight floating furnaces were drifting across the view, and it was no longer possible to see clearly. . . . Now there was gunfire—was it the random fire of the unmanned ships or the Spaniards trying to sink them before they drew closer? Perhaps both. Only daylight could reveal what was happening.

It did. Dawn showed the galleons scattered like spilled apples on the grayness of the North Sea. They had slipped their cables so hastily that not one had been caught by the fireships. That did not matter much. They had been driven out of shelter, they were open to attack, and for the time being they were unrallied, without formation.

Then it was that the great battle of the Armada began.

Almost all day the two fleets battered each other. The Spaniards fought gallantly. Many of their guns were placed too high, and they could not depress the muzzles sufficiently to aim between wind and water. So, while the English shot raked not only the decks but the waterline of their enemies, much of the

Spanish fire whined harmlessly through the canvas or the empty air. Yet, though many a galleon was pounded into silence, not one struck its colors in surrender.

All this time the Armada was being pushed steadily past Dunkirk. For the present, at any rate, it had lost its chance of combining with the Duke of Parma. About three o'clock in the afternoon the western sky over England grew suddenly livid. A fierce squall swept the North Sea. The galleons staggered as the wind struck their ragged sails. Then, some sailing out of range, others drifting helplessly toward the perilous sandbanks of the Dutch coast, they drew lamely from the battle.

For the time being the English could do little more. Their ammunition was almost gone. Some ships had scarcely a shot left to hasten the enemy on its way.

That, as it proved, was the beginning of the end. Things looked ugly for a little longer—especially when the wind changed next morning. It blew from the south now, took the still seaworthy galleons off the dangerous shoaling coast and offered them a clear run up the eastern side of England. For all their casualties, they still formed a powerful fleet; it would go hard if they landed in the unprotected north.

Luckily the wind was fickle. It shifted to the west again to bar their entrance to the Firth of Forth. It kindled the seas against them as they staggered on around the Orkneys, seeking home and safety by the longer way. It dashed ship after ship against the Hebrides and the rocky western islets of Ireland.

The English, short of food and shot, gave up the chase and left the rest to the weather. Apart from the eight vessels they had used as fireships, they had lost no craft of any kind.

One of those eight had been Drake's property, the *Thomas*. Pen in fist, he sat down to write a claim for its value, one thousand pounds, from the government.

CHAPTER VI

The Shepherd of the Ocean

THE ARMADA was destroyed by the end of August. Before autumn was out, Walter's rivalry with the Earl of Essex came to a head.

They exchanged challenges to a duel. The Court held its breath. What would happen now? The answer was soon given, for the Privy Council interfered and forbade them to fight.

It was becoming very unpleasant. While the preparations against the Armada had been going on they had seen little of each other, but now they were both at Court again, meeting daily.

Walter felt that a change of air would be advisable. He gained permission to join an expedition to raid Lisbon. That was one good turn Essex had done him, he thought with a wry smile: the Queen would now let him out of her sight, a thing she would never have allowed a year or two ago. It was Essex who must be kept at her side, like a new puppy.

Essex disliked the part of lap dog at a time like this. He slipped his leash, joined the fleet at the last moment in disguise, and sailed. He won no glory, and the Queen snubbed him when he returned by giving a gold chain to Walter for his services.

Still, it was no use pretending that things were the same as they had been. Elizabeth might quarrel with Essex, but she had a feeling for him she had never had for Walter. It was even whispered that she would consider marrying him, though he was only half her age.

Walter decided to go over to Ireland and see his estates there. They were in a sad condition, he knew, and needed his attention. His departure might have a good effect on the Queen. Time would show whether it was out of sight, out of mind, or whether absence would make the heart grow fonder.

He had taken for his Irish home the warden's house at Youghal, the little town by the mouth of the Blackwater River, on the south coast. It reminded him pleasantly of Hayes Barton and his childhood–it was long and low, with high gables and chimneys, and just such another deep projecting porch as there had been in the house where he was born. Set in its soft green garden, with the four intertwining yews and the yellow wallflowers he had planted, with its plain stone walls outside and its dark oak paneling within, it was like a gracious English manor, miraculously transported to that land of hate and sorrows.

There he had his study, wainscoted to the ceiling with fine wood carvings. There was a long table at which he wrote and a great oaken chest for his papers. Standing, pipe in hand, at the deep-set window, he could look across to the ancient tower of Saint Mary's.

But this was not peaceful, friendly Devon, and no amount of pretending could make it so. Whether as landlord of his wide estates or as Mayor of Youghal, he found his days full of worry and exasperation.

Forty thousand acres! Forty acres of red Devon land would have been more profitable.

His estates had become an unkempt jungle. The Irish would not work for the new English settlers. The government tried to force them, had no success, and gave up the useless effort.

The Irish obstinately preferred to starve rather than serve their conquerors. As Lord Burleigh admitted—he was one of the few Englishmen alive who could understand the Irish point of view—they had as much cause to hate the English as ever the Flemish had to hate Spain.

Walter had no patience with the Irish. It was the blind spot in his imagination. He could be humane and just not only to Englishmen but to other foreigners, whether friends or foes, but somehow Ireland always seemed to bring out the worst in him.

If the Irish would not be reasonable, he brooded, let them get out! He would help them to go by destroying their crops, driving them westward into the backwoods of Kerry, and bringing over Englishmen to take over the empty countryside.

Much of that plan he carried out. He imported not only farmers but Cornish tin miners to seek for metals and develop them. He brought over English lumbermen and cut timber recklessly, selling it abroad to France and Spain and Italy as barrel staves for their wine casks. But in his more honest moments he had to admit to himself that he was attempting the impossible. Ireland was too stubborn for him. She would bend, but not break. The day would come when of all his efforts nothing would remain—except the hated memory of his own name.

Life was dull at Youghal. He missed those talks in his study at Durham House. Luckily he had one intellectual neighbor, Edmund Spenser, living at

Kilcolman Castle, nearby. One day Walter rode over.

"You may not remember me," he said, "but we were at Smerwick together–you were Lord Grey's secretary."

His host's eyes warmed with pleasure. "Of course, Sir Walter! I remember well. I sent in a very favorable report about you at the time."

Walter bowed slightly, smiling. "I haven't come to exchange memories of the war, though. I've come to talk poetry."

"Excellent!" The little man sprang up delightedly, calling for wine. If Walter was bored with Irish life, Spenser was even more so. This place had been his only home for nine years, and, unless some good luck befell him, he seemed likely to end his days here.

He was a Londoner, born of poor parents, but he had managed to work his way through Cambridge. He was the same age as Walter, thirty-seven, and, like him, unmarried. The pair of them got on famously from the first handshake.

Spenser had published his *Shepherd's Calendar* a full ten years before, and Walter, after reading it, had realized that here was a great English poet, worthy to rank with the ancients.

"What are you writing now?" he demanded eagerly.

"A very long poem. . . ." Spenser hesitated and laughed. "I've been working on it since I came here nine years ago, and it isn't half finished."

Walter's eyebrows rose. He himself wrote fast. Indeed, if he had not been able to dash off his poems quickly he would never have written at all, with so many other occupations. But Spenser was not trying to be a soldier, sailor, statesman, and scientist as well.

"May I see the poem?" he asked. "What's it called?"

"*The Faerie Queen.*"

They had some splendid days and evenings after that. Spenser came over to Youghal, sat in the paneled study or paced the garden with him, admiring his cedars and the Affane cherry tree he had planted, exclaiming over the strange broad leaves of his tobacco patch.

Walter was writing, too. He did not try to compete in length, for Spenser had already written three books of *The Faerie Queen*, and had the other nine planned. Walter was content to write five or six hundred lines on "The Ocean's Love to Cynthia."

Cynthia, like Spenser's Faerie Queen, was meant for Elizabeth. Ocean was Walter, thinly disguised—

an echo of her own nickname for him. That was the accepted way to write. Courtiers like Walter must use verse to wrap up what they could not say to the Queen's face in plain prose; poets like Spenser must mingle patriotic flattery with their lines. Done well, it could still be fine poetry.

Walter wanted to please the Queen, so he pretended he loved her personally and was heartbroken when absent from her side. That was what she delighted to hear. Her taste for flattery was so blunted that, unless you laid the sugar on thickly, she was unaware of any sweetness at all.

To that extent Walter, like Shakespeare a few years afterward, had to write with his tongue in his cheek. Everyone did. But neither Walter nor Shakespeare could have written half so well if they had not also possessed the genuine instinct of the poet, forcing them to take up the pen.

So Walter wrote now of the expeditions on which he might have sailed had not the thought of her prevented him:

To seek new worlds, for gold, for praise, for glory.
To try desire, to try love severed far.
When I was gone, she sent her memory,
More strong than were ten thousand ships of war.

And so, on a similar occasion later, he was to write:

I have loved her all my youth,
But now old, as you see,
Love likes not the falling fruit
From the withered tree.

But Love is a durable fire
In the mind ever burning:
Never sick, never old, never dead,
From itself never turning.

Spenser, himself destined to rank among the greatest half-dozen names in English poetry, knew the genuine article when he saw it. He thanked God that such a man had been sent to cheer his loneliness.

Walter, however, had no wish to spend the rest of his life in Ireland. He was eager now to return to Court and see if he could win back his old place in the Queen's favor.

"You should come with me," he urged. "Bring *The Faerie Queen,* offer it to her—try your luck."

Spenser was only too willing. They crossed the Irish Sea in a frightful storm, which he described later in his poem, "Colin Clout's Come Home Again":

A world of waters heap'd up on high,
Rolling like mountains in wild wilderness,
Horrible, hideous, roaring with hoarse cry. . . .

In that poem he told, rather fancifully, how Walter had sought him out at Kilcolman:

"*One day*" (*quoth he*) "*I sat* (*as was my trade*)
Under the foot of Mole, that mountain hoar,
Keeping my sheep amongst the cooly shade
Of the green alders by the Mulla's shore;
There a strange shepherd chanced to find me out . . .
The Shepherd of the Ocean by name. . . ."

The trip was successful. The Queen was glad to see Walter back, and she was charmed with Spenser's poem, though she was not vastly impressed with its author, "this little man with little bands and little cuffs." Arrangements were quickly made to publish *The Faerie Queen.* There was a long preface addressed to Walter, who in turn contributed a couple of sonnets in praise of the book, to be printed at the beginning. And there was a dedication to "*the most magnificent empress Elizabeth.*"

That line, more than any other, ensured the success of the book. She made him Poet Laureate. Turning to the old Lord Treasurer, she said, "You will pay Mr. Spenser fifty pounds a year."

"All that for a *song*, madam?" he quavered, horrified.

"Oh . . . well, give him what is reasonable."

The old man did. As in his view that meant nothing, nothing was paid.

"Don't let it go at that," Walter advised his friend. So Spenser presented the Queen with another, and distinctly shorter, poem. It ran:

I was promised on a time
To have reason for my rhyme;
Since that time, until this season,
I have had nor rhyme nor reason.

Elizabeth saw the point, and Spenser saw his money.

All was well again at Court. Once more Walter, in shining golden armor, stood every day at the Queen's elbow. Essex was in her bad books. He had actually dared to get married. Worse than that, he had married secretly. Worst of all, the secret had come out. For a short time the Queen would have nothing to do with him.

Marriage was in the air. Spenser had gone back to Ireland, richer by a grant of three thousand acres of land there which Walter had helped to extract from the Queen. He had fallen in love with a beautiful country girl, Elizabeth Boyle, courted her with his *Amoretti* love sonnets, and married her.

The Queen was in a giving mood. She gave Walter a magnificent estate at Sherborne, in Dorset—or, to be strictly truthful, she stole it from the Church by refusing to appoint the new bishop unless he agreed to hand over the estate. She then passed it on to Walter, at a small rent, and he expressed his gratitude by giving her a jewel worth two hundred and fifty pounds. Everyone but the bishop was very pleased.

She had also agreed (more or less) to spare Walter for a few weeks for an Atlantic voyage, to attack Panama and, with any luck, to take some valuable prizes. He had nearly persuaded her last summer, when he had organized a similar venture. But at the last moment she had changed her mind, kept him at home and sent Dick Grenville instead—with disastrous results.

Dick had played the heroic fool. Walter admitted that in his heart, but he would have fought any man who had said so to his face, for he was stubbornly loyal to his cousin. So Dick died, letting a superior Spanish fleet surround him because he was too proud to run; and the Spaniards took his ship, the *Revenge*, the first English warship they had ever captured in all the years of Elizabeth's reign.

There would be no heroic foolery in this next voyage, Walter resolved. But there would be profit.

And then something happened which altered everything.

He had never cared for girls. Now in his fortieth year, he had never been in love.

On duty as Captain of the Guard, he saw a good deal of the Court ladies, and especially of the Maids of Honor, who like himself were in constant attendance on the Queen. High-born, beautiful girls they were, dressed in white and self-trained to look as though butter would not melt in their mouths. When the Queen's back was turned they relaxed this expression and were as ready to flirt and giggle as anyone else of the same age, sex, and opportunity.

Walter had no high opinion of these damsels. "Maids of Honor," he once remarked, "are like witches–they can do no good, and may do harm."

It was not therefore surprising that the Maids of Honor held an equally critical view of Walter. He was cold, inhuman, and conceited, they decided. He was a bachelor, yet he showed no interest in any of

them. Nor—even in that Court of scandal and gossip—could they link his name with anyone else.

Yet in the end it was a Maid of Honor with whom he fell in love.

Bess Throckmorton, however, was different from the others. He noticed her first because she was quiet and grave. She did not giggle in corners. She did not meet him with a look which said, "I was talking about you before you came into the room, and I shall have something more to say as soon as your back is turned."

Bess was tall and beautiful, with blue eyes and golden hair. But what most attracted him, as he gradually came to know her, was not her face but her disposition. Loveliness was common enough at Court; a character like hers was not. She was an orphan, and he saw in her much of that courage and energy which had made her dead father, Nicholas Throckmorton the diplomat, so famous.

And he realized, as he had never realized before, what a lonely man he was. Friends he had—he had a gift for friendship with other men, but not the type of men he met at Court. There he was a lonely golden figure, surrounded by jealous rivals.

He wanted something more. Someone to share his life and be a constant companion; someone to share

his new house at Sherborne and make it into a real home, such as he had never had since he left Hayes Barton as a boy; and someone who would give him children.

He moved cautiously but with speed, for his mind was made up. He must not be refused and made the laughingstock of the Court. But as day by day his official meetings with her developed into an acquaintance, and then the acquaintance into a friendship, he began to feel sure that he would not be refused.

Wasting no more time, he seized a chance to speak to her alone in an alcove of the long gallery, and in a low voice asked her to be his wife.

CHAPTER VII

Maid of Honor

BESS LOOKED AT HIM, her blue eyes wide with horror and delight.

"*Walter!* It would be wonderful—but of course it's utterly impossible. Utterly."

"Nothing's impossible."

"It would ruin you."

He shook his head. "It would make me."

"Not with the Queen." She laughed, a shade bitterly. "You know she can't bear her young courtiers to get married. Remember her fury when Essex married Frances Sidney?"

"She's forgiven him."

"But not her. Frances has to live a very retired life in the country."

Walter smiled. They stood there in the alcove, talking in low voices, pausing whenever a servant passed down the long gallery. It was typical of Court life, he thought, all this whispering in corners. He

would be glad for many reasons to get out of it. True, the palace corridors were the surest paths to greatness, but if need be he would take his chance of that to win this girl.

"And would *you* hate 'living a very retired life in the country'?" he asked.

"Not if you were there," she answered frankly.

"The Queen has just given me Sherborne, you know. I say, 'given,' " he laughed, "but it was fairly expensive, like most of her gifts. A lovely place in Dorset. . . . I think I should be happy living there, when I come back from this voyage."

"Sherborne, Dorset . . ." she said dreamily, then shook her head vigorously, so that the pearl earrings flashed softly in the candlelight. "It could never happen, Walter."

"Why ever not?" he demanded impatiently. "Essex married–and his head is still on his shoulders."

"He married Sir Philip Sidney's widow, not one of the Queen's Maids of Honor. She hates *our* getting married, too."

Walter began to say something, then pulled himself up. Anything he wanted to say about the Queen at that moment would have been high treason, and you could never be too careful. It was true,

of course, what Bess said; the Queen, never having married herself, could not bear anyone else to marry. Her young gentlemen must have eyes for her alone—it was ridiculous, for everyone knew she would be sixty next year—and her young ladies must never leave her.

Bess was plucking nervously at her flowered satin gown. "I'll have to go. Someone'll see us talking here. They'll tell her. . . ."

But Walter did not budge. "I'll let you go when you promise to be my wife," he told her bluntly.

"Oh!" His long face was full of determination. She made one last effort to resist. "It's madness," she breathed. "The Queen wouldn't *hear* of such a thing."

"She needn't hear till long afterward."

And quickly, fearing interruption at any moment, he told her his plan.

Of course, nothing could stop people from talking, least of all in Elizabeth's Court. There was gossip. Robert Cecil tackled Walter in his sly way.

"What's this I hear about you and Miss Throckmorton?"

Walter looked down at the little man guardedly. For all his undersized and crooked body, there was

more danger in Robert Cecil than in any of the big blusterers.

"What do you hear?" he inquired.

"Oh . . ." Cecil's eyes twinkled, cold and bright as a bird's. "There was talk of wedding bells."

Walter stiffened. Cecil must know nothing, or he would scurry away, talebearing to the Queen. And the Queen must know nothing—yet. If she did she would fly into a tantrum, and everything would be ruined. She had given her grudging consent for him to lead his own expedition to Panama, but she was quite capable of changing her mind. And he must, *must* go with the fleet himself. All his money was invested in the expedition. If it succeeded and captured the Spanish silver convoy, his fortune would be made forever. Then the Queen and the whole world should know the truth about him and Bess, and if they did not like it they could lump it.

But not yet.

"My dear Cecil," he said coldly, "if you hear any more gossip of that kind I do hope you'll scotch it. You can be quite sure, if any such thing were happening, I'd tell you before any man living."

"I am honored by your friendship." Was there a hint of mockery in Cecil's bow? "So you are *not* thinking of marrying and settling down?"

Walter met his searching look without a flicker. "No," he laughed, "there is no one on the face of the earth that I would be fastened to." And before Cecil could ask any more awkward questions he excused himself and strode away, his crimson cape swinging haughtily behind him.

Confound Cecil, forcing him into these pretenses! Court life was false through and through, yet without going to Court you could get nowhere. And, once at Court, you had to play its game as everyone else played it.

What had he written once? "*The result of lying is nothing else but not to be trusted of any; nor to be believed when we do speak the truth.*" And Plato had a good saying somewhere, that falsehood was not only bad in itself, it put something bad into your soul. It would rot you in the end. Oh, to be at sea again, speaking your mind freely to shipmates you could trust!

A groom led forward his horse. He mounted and rode thoughtfully home along the Strand. Lines of a poem he had written passed through his head:

> *Go, Soul, the body's guest,*
> *Upon a thankless arrant;*
> *Fear not to touch the best;*

The truth shall be thy warrant:
Go, since I needs must die,
And give the world the lie.

Say to the Court, it glows
And shines like rotten wood;
Say to the Church, it shows
What's good, and doth no good.
If Church and Court reply,
Then give them both the lie.

There had been a good many more verses, all on the same lines, and they had not made him any better liked at Court. People didn't like such things to be said in poetry—or any other way. Hypocrites!

What would Cecil have said if he'd been told the truth? That he and Bess were already secretly married—that it was too late now for even the Queen to forbid them?

He smiled grimly as he dismounted and walked into Durham House. Then, at another thought, his smile warmed and softened.

He would be in attendance on the Queen tonight. He would be seeing Bess.

It seemed almost too good to be true: in a day or two he would be off, for the first time in his life admiral of his own fleet! The royal proclamation had gone out: "*All mariners pressed to serve with Sir Walter Raleigh, Captain of Her Majesty's Guard, to repair to their ships immediately, upon pain of death. . . .*"

The Queen had tried to keep him at home. She'd wanted Sir Martin Frobisher to go instead. But the truth of the matter was, the men wouldn't follow Frobisher. He had a bad name with seamen.

"Yes," Walter thought to himself, pacing the deck of the *Roebuck* that soft May evening as she lay anchored in the lee of the Devon hills, "they may hate me at Court but not down here. I'd sooner be loved in Devon and hated in London than the other way around."

The Queen had been forced to consent at the finish. After all, she wanted the expedition to succeed—she'd put up eighteen hundred pounds herself, a tenth of the whole cost, and nearly a quarter of the tonnage. It was nothing, of course, to his own share—as he'd told Bess, he was risking every penny he possessed, and a good deal more, for he had borrowed eleven thousand pounds at interest. His flagship, the *Roebuck*, was his own.

The adventure must succeed. He had staked everything. He looked around the harbor at the twelve other ships under his command. Good craft, good men (though many of them were conscripts). . . . They would be all right under his leadership. The adventure *would* succeed.

It was not so much fun for Bess, of course, staying behind at the Queen's beck and call, still "Miss Throckmorton" to the world. But it wouldn't be for long. He would be back in no time, laden with treasure—and if he filled the Queen's lap with enough gold she'd forgive everything else.

A voice at his elbow broke in upon his thoughts, a rich, fruity Devon voice, such as it was good to hear again.

"Beg pardon, zur, but there's the London courier just come aboard. Most secret dispatches, zur, for no man's eye but yourn."

"All right, Billy, ask him to step this way."

He took the sealed package from the messenger and opened it. His face was set and calm, ready for any surprise: he had learned to hide his feelings during these past years, and if a letter were secret he gave no hint of its contents by the least exclamation or look.

"Very well," he said quietly, folded the letter, and strode away to his cabin. Only there, alone, with the door closed, did he give way to the fierce anger which swept over him.

He was to sail as admiral in charge of the expedition. That was confirmed.

But Sir Martin Frobisher would sail after him and take over the command as soon as the fleet was well out on the high seas. He himself would report back to London immediately.

Meanwhile he was to breathe no word to a living soul, lest the sailors should mutiny and refuse to weigh anchor. Such were the Queen's express orders, and he would disobey them at his peril.

Walter sat on his bunk with black disappointment washing over him like a tide. Not even the thought of seeing Bess again consoled him for the blasting of all his hopes.

Worse was to follow. He was late arriving back in London. He had sailed on the sixth of May, and Frobisher had overtaken him on the following day, according to plan, but he had stayed with the fleet for another four days, battling through a howling Biscay storm as far as Finisterre. The Queen might not like it, but he was in a sullen, defiant mood and he meant to have at least a few days at sea. If she complained, he would say that the command of a fleet couldn't be handed over in five minutes, that an admiral was not a spaniel who could be brought instantly to heel at a whistle. So he stayed until the storm clouds broke and showed the mountainous Spanish coast to port. Then he transferred to the smaller ship and turned for home.

Luckily for him he had no chance to speak his mind to the Queen. She was in no mood for it. The Biscay storm was nothing to the one which had burst at Court.

Arrived in London, he was sent to the Tower. To his alarm, he found that Bess was there too, though it was difficult to get near her. Still, ways of communication could be found. Luckily his cousin George, as Master of Ordnance in the Tower, was in charge of him, so he would not be harshly treated.

"It's a bad business," George told him sorrowfully. "Of course, you must have known there was a deal of talk about you and Miss Throckmorton. Well, suddenly it all comes to a head, Her Majesty goes off like a cannon, declares you've both behaved abominably—"

"And shuts us up in here to teach us better?"

"That's about it."

"Am I charged with anything?"

"No. And you're not deprived of any of your positions—"

"Only of my liberty," Walter cut in with a bitter laugh. "I'm still Captain of the Guard even? That's funny. Reminds me of that Roman poet, Juvenal—you know the line? *Quis custodiet ipsos custodes?* 'Who shall guard the guards themselves?' "

His cousin smiled apologetically. "I suppose that's my function. I'll make things as comfortable as I can for you, Walter. You'll be in the Brick Tower—good view of the river and the open country in the distance. You can have some of your own servants with you; you can have visitors and write letters. . . ."

"I'm sure I shall enjoy myself very much. How long is this punishment going to last?"

"I couldn't possibly say."

"Well, I can't stand being shut up. A few weeks of this place would drive me mad. How some poor devils have managed to endure it for years—!"

"You could, if you had to."

"Then God forbid I ever have to."

That was late May. June passed, and no word of forgiveness from the Queen. Walter raged in vain. Taking his morning exercise along the ramparts, he heard the royal lions roaring from their cages.

"It would save time and trouble if I were sent to feed them," he said gloomily.

If only he could get an interview with the Queen and make her see reason! But there seemed no way of making contact with her.

He racked his brains for a plan. He wrote to Cecil, knowing that she would read the letter, and filled it with sugary flatteries. "*I that was wont to behold her riding like Alexander, hunting like Diana, walking like Venus, the gentle wind blowing her fair hair about her pure cheeks like a nymph. . . .*" She would lap up such compliments as a cat laps cream, though everyone knew that the fair hair was not her own and her cheeks were painted.

Nothing happened. Perhaps the Queen would take pity if she heard that he had tried to kill himself? So, with the help of Cousin George and Arthur Gorges, he staged a suicide attempt–it was so realistic that Arthur's knuckles got slashed with the dagger, but luckily Arthur was a distant relative, too, and was willing to lose a little blood to help the family.

Her Majesty must have heard all about it (George concocted a marvelous letter, describing all that had happened and a good deal more that had not), but she remained unmoved. All through the August heat, with the plague raging in the city slums outside, Walter remained a prisoner in the fortress.

Deliverance came from a most unexpected quarter: in a sense, it was his ships that rescued him.

The *Roebuck* had captured a Portuguese East Indiaman off the Azores—the huge *Madre de Dios*, a seven-decker floating castle, with a crew of eight hundred and a cargo valued at half a million pounds. Early in September this colossal prize was towed into Dartmouth.

The news flashed through England. Never had such wealth been gathered in a single vessel. There were over five hundred tons of precious spices—cinnamon and cloves, nutmeg and mace, cochineal and benjamin. The pepper alone was worth over a hundred thousand pounds. As for precious stones, pearls, amber, and musk, the full value would never be known.

For an excellent reason. Merchants and dealers of all kinds, honest and otherwise, flocked to Dartmouth from every part of England like ravens to a carcass. The sailors who had risked their lives to capture the ship were determined to have first pick of the contents, especially as the quays were crowded with men offering ready cash for anything they could smuggle ashore. One sailor was caught with a chain of pearls, two chains of gold, four crystal spoons set with gold and gems, and a fistful of other valuables. Another had a bag containing three hundred diamonds. It was doubtful how much would be left by the time the Queen's officers managed to restore order and check the cargo.

Walter heard the news in the Tower, and sat seething with helpless rage. It would serve the Queen right, of course, but that was a poor consolation. He had heard Robert Cecil's despairing comment, "So far as the jewels, pearls, and amber are concerned, I fear the birds are flown." Wasn't there a man among them who could check this wild looting?

There was a knock, the door opened, and Sir George Carew was standing there with another man.

"Walter, you're to ride down to Devon immediately. Mr. Blunt here is to go with you—that's just a formality. We have horses saddled."

Walter got up slowly. "You mean—Dartmouth?"

His cousin nodded. "It's the Queen's order. Cecil himself says there's no other man in England can clear up that mess. The sailors seem to have gone crazy, but they'll listen to you."

"Yes, they'll listen to me." Walter laughed stormily. He stretched himself exultantly, as if actual chains had dropped from his limbs. "Come along, Mr. Blunt. You're my keeper but it's your business to keep up with me. I warn you, I shall ride like a fury—and if I meet any of these looters on the road I mean to strip them as naked as ever they were born."

CHAPTER VIII

The Castle in the West

MATTERS WERE STRAIGHTENED OUT at Dartmouth. Walter saved all he could and twice what any other man could have saved, tactfully making sure that the Queen got far more than her fair share when the prize money was divided. He favored her at his own expense. So far from gaining by the expedition, he was himself out of pocket. But if the Queen forgave him, the sacrifice would be worth while.

"*Fourscore thousand pounds*," he wrote to the Lord Treasurer, "*is more than ever a man presented Her Majesty as yet. If God have sent it for my ransom, I hope Her Majesty will accept it.*"

She did, but without a word of thanks or forgiveness. He was free of the Tower, he remained Captain of the Guard, but he was not to show his face at Court. So he went down to Dorset with Bess to take possession of their new home.

He had fallen in love with Sherborne Castle at

first sight. Indeed, he had fallen literally, through his horse's stumbling, as he galloped past on one of his official journeys between Plymouth and London. He had plowed the mud painfully with his face, but, as one of his half-brothers reminded him, something similar had happened to William the Conqueror when he landed on the English beach. It might be a good omen now, as then.

At last it was his, a Norman keep, surrounded by a wall with four massive towers, standing on a rocky hillock nearly fifty feet high. A strong place, defended by a thirty-foot moat and marshy ground on three sides, so that the only approach to the fortified gatehouse was by way of a narrow causeway. One way, the windows looked down Long Street to the old Abbey at the far end. In other directions he could gaze over the deer park and the open countryside.

He had never been happier than he was in those first days at Sherborne, exploring with Bess and discussing all the improvements they would make.

"There's a lot of repair work needed," he said.

"But we can make it very comfortable." Bess spoke confidently. The more she saw of the place, however, the more she realized that it had been built at a time when strength was more important than comfort. It must have been fine in the Wars of the Roses, a century ago. In these modern times she would have preferred larger windows and wider passages. Fortresses were out of fashion.

Walter saw the little shiver she could not help. He, too, believed in civilized living. "No," he said decisively, "I've changed my mind—we'll stop the repairs and build an entirely new house in the park next door."

Once he had that idea there was no checking him. Delighted, but worried about the expense of it all, Bess tried to enter into the spirit of the new plan, and soon she was as fully devoted to it as he was.

"We'll plant orchards," he said.

"And a modern garden, Walter!"

"And some long avenues—"

"Limes, Walter—they smell so sweet!"

"And I like beeches, they look fine when the leaves turn. We'll plant a grove near the house."

"With a stone seat at the far end—"

"If you like. And, Bess, we'll have trees and shrubs that no one else in England has—I'll get my captains to bring them in wet moss, cedars from Virginia, shrubs from the islands! We'll coax them to grow here."

She laughed. "We'll be growing tobacco soon!"

"Why not? And you must have water in your garden, unless . . ." he paused with a smile, "unless you have too much 'Water' already?"

"I can never have too much," she answered seriously.

"Then we'll divert some from the river, we'll run it through rocks into the garden—"

"Stop, dear! We're building a house, not a county."

"You'll see," he promised her.

And sure enough, within the next year or two it had all come true.

Kit Marlowe, the young playwright, had written romantically of country life:

Come, live with me, and be my love,
And we will all the pleasures prove,
That hills and valleys, dales and fields,
Or woods, or steepy mountain yields . . . .

And I will make thee beds of roses,
And a thousand fragrant posies,
A cap of flowers, and a kirtle
Embroidered all with leaves of myrtle.

Walter had answered him with friendly mockery:

Thy gowns, thy shoes, thy beds of roses,
Thy cap, thy kirtle, and thy posies,
Soon break, soon wither, soon forgotten,
In folly ripe, in reason rotten . . . .

But, could youth last, and love still breed,
Had joys no date, nor age no need,
Then these delights my mind might move,
To live with thee, and be thy love.

But now for a time, with Bess at Sherborne, he felt that Kit had scarcely exaggerated the happiness of living in the country with one's beloved.

It was a busy life, with little chance to grow bored. He had to see to the building and planting of the estate, and there were tenant farmers to deal with. He had to sit on the magistrates' bench and try all sorts of people, from sturdy vagabonds to poor old women accused of witchcraft. When the judge came to hold his Assizes at Dorchester he must be in his place with the other gentlemen of the county, and every Sunday, unless he was away in London, he escorted Bess to morning service in the Abbey church, where they had a family pew in the side chapel of Saint Katherine. He was Ranger of the Royal Forest of Gillingham, responsible for "trees blown down by wind, trees felled for timber, trees dry and dead, old hedges and coppices, and dead underwood."

Friends came often to visit them. Bess proved an excellent hostess; Walter could look after the talk, so she took care of the table. "I hope your Lordship will be here tomorrow or Saturday," Walter wrote to Lord Cobham, "or else my wife says her oysters will all be spoiled, and her partridge stale."

He went to London frequently, staying at Durham House, which was still his. Though he was forbidden the Queen's presence, he remained Captain of her Guard and had to manage its affairs as best he could. And, being M.P. for Devon, he attended Parliament whenever it was called together.

There, one day, he made an eloquent speech to defend a man's right to hold what religious ideas he liked. There was a savage bill before the House, urging the death penalty for a harmless sect of Puritans called the Brownists.

"The law is hard," he told the House of Commons, "if it take a man's life, or banishes him, on a jury's opinion of what he believes or does not believe."

He himself was passionately in favor of free thought and free speech. He was as ready to defend a Catholic at one end of the scale as a Puritan at the other. For himself, he belonged to the Church of England, but he did not swallow its teaching without due thought. And that very fact, as it proved, brought more trouble upon him.

It was highly dangerous to think for yourself just then, either in religion or in politics. If, to cap everything, you showed too much interest in astronomy, chemistry, and other branches of science, you were well on the road to being accused of heresy or witchcraft.

His friend, Dr. Dee, had barely escaped from an angry mob twenty years before; as it was, they had wrecked his house and all his equipment. Even in Sherborne people still pointed out the house of Maturyn Bensart, who was said to have raised the dead and cast metal images of men and women he wished to injure. Bensart had been examined by the Church court of the time, but fortunately they had discovered no evidence of such activities.

In London, Walter and his group of friends were the center of much gossip. Old Dr. Dee, of course, was notorious—in a sense the man asked for trouble, with his crystal gazing and spiritualism added to less sensational studies. But people were almost equally suspicious of well-balanced men like Tom Hariot, who used a telescope before Galileo did, made brilliant discoveries in mathematics, and corresponded with all the leading scientists in Europe. Lord Derby was in the group; interested alike in poetry and chemistry, he was believed to dabble in witchcraft. Lord Northumberland, who studied the same subjects and was eccentric in his manner, was nicknamed the Wizard Earl.

Gossip burst into open scandal with the mysterious death of Kit Marlowe.

Kit had been one of the outstanding younger members of the group. He had lived and talked with the same wild passion as marked his poetry, coming out with remarks about God and the Bible which were rank blasphemy. He had made further enemies by acting as a secret service agent.

On May 18, 1593, he was summoned before the Privy Council to answer a charge of atheism: he was said to have given a private lecture to Sir Walter Raleigh and others, proving by logical arguments that God did not exist.

Kit would probably have talked himself out of danger. It was likely enough the charge was true, but the evidence was poor. He was still a free man twelve days later when, in a staged tavern quarrel at Deptford, he was silenced by a murderer's dagger.

The mystery of his death was never solved. Like as not, it was due to his secret service activities and had nothing to do with the Privy Council affair. But many people blamed Walter and his friends. A few went so far as to hint that they had removed Kit to stop his mouth forever: dead men told no tales. The more reasonable ones pitied him as a young man who had got into bad company and been ruined, the "bad company" being those who gathered in the turret study at Durham House or sought the country air at Sherborne.

There was more and more talk of "Sir Walter Raleigh's school of atheism," in which youths were led astray by older men who should have known better. Walter, as usual, shrugged his shoulders. Had not the Greek philosopher Socrates, one of the best and wisest men who had ever lived, been accused of the selfsame charge?

"And wasn't he condemned for it–and put to death?" pointed out one of his more cautious friends.

Walter said nothing.

Soon he was attacked in a comedy on the London stage. (Something similar, he remembered, had happened to Socrates in Athens two thousand years earlier.) Walter's circle of friends, his so-called school of atheism, was represented as "the School of Night." He himself was caricatured under the name of "Don Adriano de Armado, a fantastical Spaniard" —a widely traveled, melancholy liar, who spoke to his servant with the accent not of Spain but of Devon. The play was entitled *Love's Labor Lost,* and the author was a young man ambitious to take Kit Marlowe's place in the theater. By name Will Shakespeare.

It was in Dorset, however, not in London, that the situation developed most dangerously. Walter had a quiet way of shocking people in conversation, very different from Kit's wild speeches, but no more popular with the solemn prigs against whom he used it.

One evening, after dinner at a neighbor's house, Walter started a serious discussion on the human soul, and turned to a rather pompous clergyman, the Reverend Ralph Ironside, for an expert opinion.

"Though I was at Oxford myself," he admitted, "and debated these things in the schools, so far I have never been satisfied on this point: what *is* the soul?"

Mr. Ironside coughed, studied his wineglass and coughed again. The party waited patiently. "It's defined in Aristotle," he said importantly. "If you read Aristotle's *De Animo*, the first chapter—"

"Aristotle is obscure and intricate," Walter objected. "Couldn't you explain it in plain English for us?"

"Well—er—" Mr. Ironside racked his brain for a convenient quotation. "The soul, Sir Walter, is a spiritual and immortal substance breathed into man by God."

Walter inclined his head courteously. "Yes," he persevered, "but what *is* that spiritual and immortal substance?"

"The soul," retorted the clergyman, nettled.

Walter rolled his eyes despairingly to the ceiling. His courtesy was sorely tried, for he never suffered fools gladly. "Really, you don't reason like a scholar," he protested, "you're arguing in a circle."

"Arguments about first principles *must* go in circles."

"Not in mathematics. In mathematics you can prove your arguments."

The discussion went on for some time, and got warmer. But the clergyman could not be persuaded to argue on scientific lines, and his mind continued to go around in circles. Walter saw they were wasting time and stood up from the table. "Shall we say grace?" he suggested coldly. "It would be better than this discussion."

Mr. Ironside did not forget that evening when he had been made to feel small. He discussed matters with other parsons in the district. In March, ten months after Kit's death, a commission of inquiry was summoned at the little town of Cerne Abbas, a few miles south of Sherborne. Its duty was to investigate reports that a set of atheists existed in the neighborhood.

Mr. Ironside gave evidence and repeated that conversation with Walter. Other witnesses appeared with various stories, mostly trivial. One of Walter's friends, Thomas Allen, had torn leaves from a Bible and dried tobacco on them. The same man's servant, when discussing the sermon after church, had remarked that it might have been shorter. Marlowe had jokingly boasted that he could rewrite the New Testament in better Greek. Walter's brother Carew had once commandeered a parson's horse for public business; when he complained that he must get home to preach a sermon, Carew had unsympathetically suggested that the horse could preach it for him.

One could say that such remarks were in bad taste, irreverent, and some perhaps almost blasphemous, but they did not prove that Walter kept a school of atheists. Against him personally the commission could find nothing serious at all. To have made Mr. Ironside look foolish was not yet a hanging matter.

But Bess at least was vastly relieved when the commission finished its business and wound up with no harm done. Walter had so many enemies. . . . They would have used any possible weapon that came to their hands.

This peaceful life in Dorset could not go on forever. It was too good to be true.

It was. Walter's restless spirit would not forever be satisfied with mere visits to London for Parliament or the meetings of Archbishop Parker's Society of Antiquaries, with trips to Bath for the medicinal waters or to Weymouth for sea bathing. He was tireless. He liked to sleep only five hours, to read for two, and to converse with friends for another two. The remaining fifteen hours of every day he expected to fill with action.

Somehow he must regain the Queen's favor and step back into the world where great action was possible. What could he do?

At last the answer came in one word: Guiana.

CHAPTER IX

In Quest of El Dorado

It was said that a vast and wealthy Indian empire existed in the secret inland places of Guiana. When the Spanish conquerors looted Peru, the Incas had retreated there, carrying their richest treasures. There was more wealth in this mysterious region than in Mexico and Peru put together. Gold dust was so common that hundreds of courtiers could anoint themselves and then gild their bodies until they shone golden from head to foot, and so sit drinking at the emperor's feast. Manoa was the capital city, but men spoke of it as the land of El Dorado, "the Golden Man."

Was it a fairy tale?

If so, Walter was not the only man to believe in it. The Spanish government believed in it. They had sent out no fewer than twenty-seven expeditions to find it—so far without success. Their governor in Trinidad, Antonio de Berreo, had just written a hopeful report on the subject. A copy had been captured and brought to Walter by a ship's captain who worked for him.

He talked it over with his friend, Laurence Kemys. Laurence had a brilliant intellect: he had been made a Fellow of Balliol College even before taking his degree. He was learned in geography—and he had no doubt that El Dorado existed. In fact, he was willing to give up his comfortable position in England and join the expedition.

Only Bess disbelieved and disapproved.

One could hardly blame her. Like most wives, she would have the nerve-racking part of waiting at home, wondering if she would ever see her husband again. She sympathized with Walter, she sometimes felt guilty because she had ruined his career by marrying him, and she wished desperately that he *could* find his way back into the Queen's good books.

But not this way! Like Hamlet, Bess would

> *. . . rather bear those ills we have*
> *Than fly to others that we know not of.*

She tried to persuade Walter, but he had the bit between his teeth. Perhaps he would listen to Robert Cecil—he would *have* to listen to Robert, and Robert had always been her good friend. She wrote to him:

"I hope for my sake you will rather draw Sir Walter toward the east than help him forward toward the sunset. . . . You great councilors are so full of new counsels, but we poor souls, that have bought sorrow at a high price, desire and can be pleased with the same misfortune we hold, fearing alterations will but multiply misery, of which we have already felt sufficient."

It was no good. Walter went ahead with his plans. The government approved the voyage, the royal patent was signed, though Walter was described in it only as "our servant," not as "our trusty and well-beloved servant." The Queen was slow to forgive. She gave him permission to discover and conquer any lands not yet possessed by a Christian nation, and to drive out anyone who tried to settle within six hundred miles of any colony he founded.

Their first baby was born while all these preparations were in hand. They called him Walter, Wat for short.

A few months later the little fleet of five ships went staggering out into the February grayness of the Atlantic. At least, thought Bess, clutching her tiny son, at least I have *you.* I can't be robbed of *you.*

She had yet to learn, in bitter afterdays, that she could.

Six weeks later they saw the three sharp peaks of Trinidad black against the sunset sky.

This small, square island lay facing the immense delta of the Orinoco River, whose myriad channels twisted through mangrove swamps stretching nearly two hundred miles along the coast of the mainland. That steamy, sinister maze was the gateway to El Dorado.

"But first," said Walter, "we'll have a look at the island."

It was good to stretch their legs after the voyage, to drink cool spring water and sample unknown fruits. It was the first time Walter had set foot on American soil. It seemed strange, that. He had thought about America ever since he could remember, dreamed of the Northwest Passage, paid for expeditions . . . but only now, when he was past forty, was he seeing it for himself.

He was a poor walker in that tropical heat, but he was tireless in exploring the wonders of the island. He was especially struck by the lake of pitch, but everything—plants, animals, foods, Indian customs—was full of interest.

From the Indians there was nothing to fear. They came to the English camp and offered friendship. Walter was always ready to talk with them. He was sorry for the way they had been treated by the Spaniards, who had usually behaved as though the natives of America were less than animals.

Theirs was a black record, he had always known. They had landed in Jamaica in 1503, and by 1558 there was not a native alive there. They had taken Haiti in 1508, and forty years had reduced the natives from sixty thousand to five hundred. In Guiana the Spanish Governor, Antonio de Berreo, had behaved so cruelly that the Indians had risen against him. He had been forced to retire to Trinidad.

Now Walter saw the position with his own eyes. The friendly Indians stopped coming in daylight. They crept to his tent secretly under cover of night.

"If the Governor learns," they explained, "he will hang us. He has hanged several of our friends who came to you last week."

"I think," said Walter slowly to Kemys, "we had better pay a visit to this Spanish gentleman."

"We must go carefully. We don't want to stir up a hornets' nest behind us when we go upriver."

"True. But we don't want to leave a dangerous enemy untouched."

It was a pity they had lost contact with three of their ships and the expedition had been reduced to two. However, they managed to surprise Berreo in his settlement, take him prisoner, and set free five Indian chiefs whom he had tortured and almost starved to death. Walter called a great meeting of the natives, showed them a picture of Queen Elizabeth, and explained that she had sent him to save them from Spanish rule. It was not his fault that this did not actually happen.

He was tempted to hang Berreo, who richly deserved it. But, as Kemys had said, they must go carefully. With their present small numbers, they must not infuriate the Spanish government. Besides, Berreo might be more useful alive. He would be a hostage, and he might possess information about El Dorado.

He did. Sitting at dinner with the Englishmen, more like an honored guest than a prisoner, he held forth on his own efforts to find the lost empire, not knowing that Walter had already seen a copy of his official report and that the English expedition was on the same quest.

"This is all very interesting," said Kemys quietly. "It's a great pity no one has ever *seen* this place."

It was a lucky shot. "You are mistaken, señor,"

retorted the Governor swiftly. "Somebody has."

Walter and his friend exchanged glances over their wine cups. This was interesting! The fish was nibbling. They must be gentle in case he took fright.

"Indeed?" said Walter, studying his fingernails. "May one ask who? I suppose it's just another Indian's story?"

"Far from it, Sir Walter." Berreo smiled triumphantly. "It was a Spanish officer, Juan Martínez de Albujar. He was captured by Indians on the Orinoco, taken to the Emperor, and received most kindly. He stayed in his capital for over six months."

Walter leaned forward, trying to hide his excitement. The other officers around the table had fallen silent. Everyone was listening intently.

"And was Manoa the wonderful city we have been told it is, Your Excellency?"

"More wonderful! It was over a day's journey from the outskirts of the city to the Emperor's palace. Even the kitchen utensils were of gold and silver."

"Not very practical for cooking," Kemys suggested.

Berreo was ready for that. "The boiling pots and so forth had copper mixed with the silver," he admitted, "but that was only to give strength, it was not due to any lack of gold. Martínez saw giant statues of gold, he saw an artificial garden with trees and flowers of gold and silver . . . why, he said that bars of gold lay around like heaps of firewood!"

"Hasn't he been able to show you the way back?" asked Walter.

The Governor spread his olive palms regretfully. "Alas, no! He was taken there blindfold and brought out the same way. It was a fortnight's journey."

"But he started from the delta of the Orinoco yonder?"

"Yes."

Walter smiled. "Then so far we are on the right track."

Berreo's dark eyes widened. "Y-you mean, Sir Walter—you mean that you, too, are in search of El Dorado?" He turned to the others. "Gentlemen, this is madness! You must try to persuade Sir Walter. You have no idea of the dangers and hardships—the jungle monsters, the insects, the savage Indians—"

"We may find the Indians more helpful than you do," said Kemys sharply, and someone else added, "Where a Spaniard has been, an Englishman can go."

"We shall do our best," said Walter.

They started a few days later, taking a hundred men in five boats, with stores for a month.

Berreo had not exaggerated the discomfort. The ocean voyage had been a pleasure cruise by comparison—however cramped the ships, at least they offered shelter against rain and sun. In the boats they had no protection against either, and there was nothing half-hearted about the weather of South America: they were grilled by the sun and soaked by sheets of rain alternately. The food stank, and there were no facilities for preparing it properly.

They were two hundred and fifty miles from the sea. The unbelievable river was still four miles wide and nearly four hundred feet deep. They struggled on, the men sweating at the oars.

"I've been in a few prisons," one tough sailor admitted with a grin, "but they was all like living in palaces compared with this hell on earth."

Walter was not enjoying it. He had lived roughly in his time, especially during the French and Irish wars—he had even tasted prison life—but he had never been through anything like this. Still less had Kemys. Often he sighed for his quiet study at Oxford and the noble dinners at high table in Balliol hall, but he did not complain. El Dorado would be worth it.

Things soon took a happier turn. They landed, pitched camp, and were visited by a friendly Indian chief. He was an amazing old gentleman—he claimed to be a hundred and ten years of age, and to have walked the fourteen miles from his home. He brought a multitude of his subjects with him and, what was even more welcome, heaps of food. The expedition sat down to a superb banquet, with pork, chicken, venison, pineapples and other delicious fruits, all washed down with native beer. Walter was given an armadillo as a present, and had it cooked for dinner the next day. It was a weird creature, but he was always ready to try anything once, and one was not forced to eat its armor plates as well.

Old Topiawari knew the Spanish Governor. "He murdered my nephew," he said grimly. "He dragged me in chains for seventeen days." As for Manoa, the City of Gold, if Walter would leave him a force of Englishmen to fight Berreo, he would lead the party to their destination himself.

"And I think he would," laughed Kemys when, after the banquet, the old gentleman started gallantly on his fourteen-mile walk home. But it was quite impossible to give him the force he asked for, and

Walter could only promise to come back next year with a stronger party.

They took to their boats again and battled their way upriver till they reached a point where the Caroni joined the Orinoco. Most of the clues suggested that it was by this route that they would come to El Dorado.

But the Caroni proved unnavigable. The current ran like a millrace. The rowers strained and cursed, but they could make no headway.

"It's no good," said Kemys, "we'll have to land and go forward on foot."

Walter nodded. He knew, though, that he would not get far. They were none of them fit for long marches in this climate, he himself least of all. And the season was getting late. Any day now, they had been warned, storms and torrential rains would bring floods and make returning as difficult as advancing.

They landed and trudged across the level ground to where a ridge of hills promised them a view. When they reached the crest one of the men shouted and pointed:

"Look, sir—what's that? Smoke?"

They all stared, shading their eyes. It was no slender column, such as might have come from a campfire. It was a widely spread haze above the tree-tops.

For a wild moment Walter hoped. He had seen a smoke haze like that before, over a big city. He had looked down from his window in the Tower and seen it over London. Could there be a city here? Could it be—possibly—Manoa?

"Listen," said Kemys. "Is that thunder?"

No, it was too steady a noise. It went on all the time, an incessant booming.

"It must be a waterfall," said Walter. "In which case that isn't smoke, it's spray."

He proved to be right. But what a waterfall! There was not one—there were a dozen, one above the other, each as high as a church tower. It was no wonder the river just below had been running so strong. . . .

And there, for the time being, they had to turn back. The weather broke that night with a terrific thunderstorm and cloudbursts. The Orinoco seethed like a pot coming to the boil. They were four hundred miles from the coast, and if they delayed longer even the downstream journey might become impossible.

They had not found El Dorado—this time. But they had gained much useful information, made friends with the Indians, and collected specimens of rock that seemed to contain gold. Unluckily, they had no proper tools for prospecting, but had to gather these samples as best they could with their fingers and daggers.

"At least," said Walter, "we know there's gold there."

The Queen and her Council might care nothing for colonies, but gold was something they appreciated. The man who found it would be listened to.

CHAPTER X

The Rivals

WALTER'S ENEMIES were waiting for him. They were quite determined he should never regain the Queen's favor. He was still, in name, the Captain of the Guard, though banned from appearing in her presence. If he had hoped that his voyage to Guiana would break the ban, he was disappointed.

"It's fantastic!" he stormed to Bess. "These liars will stop at nothing."

"What it it now?" she inquired patiently.

"Some of them are suggesting I've never *been* to Guiana–it's whispered that I've spent the whole seven months hidden in Cornwall!"

"But–the gold ore you brought back, the Indian boy Gualtero–"

"Oh, I'm supposed to have bought those," he said with a bitter laugh. "And no doubt I've bribed Kemys and the rest of them to back my story. It can all be explained away." He paced the room excitedly. "I must go back there, Bess."

"No. Walter, please!"

"I must."

"In Heaven's name, why?"

"I promised those poor Indians. They trusted me. And there were two of our lads stayed behind with Topiawari, to learn the language. I can't leave them to rot in the jungle. And that's not the main thing—there's an empire to be won there for the Queen, if only she'd listen."

He wrote an account of the expedition, entitled *Discovery of the Large and Beautiful Empire of Guiana.* It was a tremendous success in England, and was quickly published in French, Dutch, and Latin. Still the Queen and her Council did not rise to the bait.

But other events were stirring now. He found he could not possibly go back to Guiana just then, but he sent Kemys with two ships instead. Kemys came home more enthusiastic than ever, declaring that he would devote the rest of his life to the country, which he insisted on naming Raleana. He had charted the coast, listed the rivers, and found evidence of another gold mine at Mount Aio, much nearer the sea.

Walter could do little more just then. A powerful expeditionary force was being collected against

Spain, and the Council had offered him a chance he would have been a fool to miss.

The actual purpose of the voyage was kept a close secret. Walter knew it, for both he and Cousin George Carew (as Master of the Ordnance) were on the Council of Five advising the two supreme commanders, Lord Howard as admiral and the Earl of Essex as general.

The objective was the Spanish naval base of Cadiz. But it was to be no mere raid, no "singeing of the King of Spain's beard" such as Francis Drake had carried out years ago. They were to capture the city itself, and–if Essex had his way–even to hold it as a permanent English outpost in Spain.

Essex and Walter were still rivals, though often they were forced to seem friendly enough on the surface. It was hard not to feel jealous of Essex–what opportunities he had had compared with Walter! Walter had been compelled to make his own way in life, fighting at every step; he, at the age of eight, had become Earl of Essex, Earl of Ewe, Viscount Hereford, Lord Ferrers of Chartley, Bourchier, and Lovaine . . . and Lord knew what else.

Give the fellow his due, he was tall, dashing, gallant, a bold rider at tournament, an energetic general, a fine scholar. . . . It was small wonder he had captured the Queen's heart when he came to Court as a youth.

Since then they had both blotted their copybooks by getting married. But she had never been able to treat him as she had treated Walter. Essex, after all, was one of the foremost noblemen in England, with powerful friends everywhere, at home and abroad. Even so, she had managed to keep him in the background lately, and now, like Walter, he was hoping that the Spanish expedition would put him back in the center of the picture.

Essex was busy now at Plymouth, forming his regiments. Walter went hunting ships and men along the Thames estuary. The Earl sent him a friendly letter, ending:

"*I will wish and pray for a good wind for you. And when you are come, I will make you see I desire to do you as much honor, and give you as great contentment, as I can. For this is the action and the time in which you and I shall be both taught to know and love one another, and so I wish you all happiness and rest,*

Your very assured friend,

Essex

"When you come, I will show you the fairest troops for their number that ever were looked upon."

That did not prevent his writing to Robert Cecil and complaining against Walter because, in spite of favorable winds, he had not brought the ships from the Thames mouth. Actually Walter was having a hard time collecting seamen, who melted away on one excuse or another as soon as he had enrolled them. He had to tour the low taverns along the river himself, in mud and rain, to gather what crews he could.

When at last he brought his ships around to Plymouth, he found the atmosphere at headquarters was distinctly thundery. Essex was furious with everyone, from the Queen (who was shilly-shallying as to who should command, after all, and whether the expedition should sail or disband) down to young Arthur Throckmorton, Bessie's brother, whom he had ordered from the table during an argument and placed under arrest. He was on bad terms with his fellow commander, the Lord Admiral, a much older man, who had disliked his action in signing his name first on a joint letter to the Council. Lord Howard had taken a penknife and cut out the signature.

It was a wonderful expedition, thought Walter with a wry smile as he surveyed the regiments paraded on the Hoe and the ships covering the blue surface of the Sound. A positive armada—ninety-six English vessels, twenty-four Dutch, and nearly seventeen thousand men, including a thousand gentlemen volunteers.

But with such rivalries and jealousies running through the expedition from top to bottom, between the commanders, between army and navy, between English and Dutch, how would it all turn out, triumph or disaster?

They sailed on the first of June. Each captain had his sealed orders, inscribed, "*If you be separated from the fleet by foul weather or otherwise, you shall herein find to what place you shall repair, till when you shall not open the enclosed upon pain of death.*" Inside was written the secret rendezvous—Cadiz.

Lord Howard led the first of the five squadrons in the *Ark Royal*, Essex the second in the *Due Repulse*. Walter led the fourth squadron in the *Warspite*, with Cousin George in the *Mary Rose*, with the *Dreadnought* and the *Nonpareil*, the *Rainbow* and the *Lion* and nearly twenty other ships under his command.

During the day the fleet spread widely across the Bay of Biscay, far as the eye could reach. At dusk each squadron fell in behind its flagship, following the gleam of its stern lantern throughout the night. When the commanders wanted to consult with the Council of Five they fired a gun and hoisted the arms of England. Walter then had to order a boat and be rowed across to the *Ark Royal.* When the flag of Saint George went up, it meant a general conference of all ship's captains.

They held one of those when they were ten days out, to discuss where they were. No one could tell for certain. Some thought one thing, some another. By striking a rough average they came to the conclusion they were in latitude 42 degrees, opposite the point where the northern frontier of Portugal met Spain, and rather less than a hundred miles west of the coast.

"Thank God the weather's calm," said Walter. "It makes for slow sailing, but at least we can keep the fleet together."

They crept southward. A week later they fell in with an Irish merchantman, newly out of Cadiz. The Spaniards had not heard a whisper of their coming, the garrison was weak, and the fortifications in process of rebuilding. Best news of all, the merchant convoy was about to sail for the West Indies—forty great ships, stuffed with merchandise. True, there was a naval escort with them, a fleet of powerful galleons, but if all went well they would only increase the value of the prize.

Another council of war was arranged. Walter could not go, for his squadron was told off to sweep the coast for stray Spanish vessels which might otherwise escape.

When he came back he found, to his horror, that they had decided to land the troops and attack the town, leaving the galleons untouched. Despite his years of soldiering, Walter always thought of himself rather as a naval man, and now, as a naval man, he felt that this plan was suicide. They might easily lose every man jack they put ashore, wreck the whole expedition, and—worst of all—leave England defenseless against that Spanish invasion which was always a possibility just around the corner.

The wind was rising, the waves mounting. Two of the first landing craft were capsized. With his own eyes, he saw the men drowning, weighed down with their iron breastplates and heavy boots. He saw, too, the Spanish garrison hurrying down to the beach to contest the landing.

Something must be done to prevent disaster. He

called for his boat and leaped into it as it bobbed and tossed against his flagship's side.

It was taking a big chance. Essex was quick tempered at the best of times, and he was senior to Walter. But it was better to risk a snub from his rival than a catastrophe for the expedition.

"Row me to the *Due Repulse*," he said between his teeth.

"Aye, aye, sir!"

The boat shoved off. With difficulty, in that rough sea, they labored around to the Earl's flagship. A rope ladder came snaking through the air; Walter grasped it and began to climb. He wondered what sort of a welcome he would get when Essex saw him.

The young general was on the poop, directing the operations. He looked worried, and so did his staff. Walter came straight to the point.

"I know," said Essex, "but I can't help it. Lord Howard refuses to take the fleet into the bay until we've stormed the town and silenced the shore batteries."

"But it's madness–it means general ruin."

"Sir Walter's quite right," one of the officers put in. "Half of us will be drowned before we set foot on the beach, and the Spaniards'll deal with the rest.

Twenty men could hold the beach against us with hese breakers running."

"I can't go against the Lord Admiral," Essex persisted. "He's thinking about the Queen's ships—you know what she's like. No matter how big the victory, she expects to get her own ships safely back. Look here, Sir Walter, as you weren't at the meeting when this was decided, you've a perfect right to go and state your views to Howard. Persuade him if you can. For my part, I'll be only too glad."

"I'll do my best."

Again Walter swung down the heaving side of the ship, made the dangerous jump into the shifting boat, and was rowed away in the direction of the *Ark Royal*. Again he wondered what sort of a welcome he would get for his interference.

Lord Howard took it well. When he had heard Walter's opinion he agreed to cancel the landing. He asked Walter to write out his own suggested plan for an attack by sea and submit it by midnight.

Walter turned back toward his own flagship. As the boat passed under the quarter of the *Due Repulse*, the Earl and his staff leaned over the carved bulwarks and shouted, "What's the news?"

Walter answered in one exultant word of Spanish, "*Entramos!*"—"We're going in!"

Essex grinned like a boy, pulled off his plumed hat and hurled it delightedly into the sea.

Walter's plan was accepted; he was given the honor of leading the attack, and at the first peep of day he led his squadron into the channel.

A great array of galleons, galleys, frigates, and other Spanish warships were marshaled against them, and there were forts and shore batteries scouring the water from all sides. Walter sailed the *Warspite* into the thick of their fire, not sending a shot in answer to their broadsides but acknowledging each with a scornful blare of the trumpet. Only when the outlying Spanish squadron turned and ran for shelter, offering a perfect target, did he open fire.

"We'll bestow a benediction among them," he said with a grim smile. "But," he added, pointing to the mighty *Saint Philip*, "that's our *real* target. There are men in that ship who saw Dick Grenville die. We've a score to settle there."

He laid the *Warspite* alongside the Spanish flagship, and for nearly three hours they battered one another ferociously. Seeing their leader's danger, other Spanish ships closed in and concentrated their fire on the *Warspite*.

It was hot work. Walter grew worried. His own

plan had provided that two flyboats, for boarding, should be detailed to each galleon, and should move in, like terriers, as soon as the Spaniards were battered enough. It was strictly forbidden to board direct from his own ship. The Queen's vessels must not be risked in such enterprises.

But where could the flyboats be? There was no sign of them anywhere. Meanwhile the *Warspite* herself was in a bad way. It was a tossup whether she would sink or take fire. The *Saint Philip* must be dealt with at once.

He took his boat and rowed hastily to Essex. Essex tried to dissuade him: the Spanish ship was full of troops, they would heavily outnumber the *Warspite's* company. "But if you insist," he promised, "I'll come to your help myself."

He had been away only a quarter of an hour, but when he got back he saw that his ship had dropped into third place. The *Nonpareil* and the *Rainbow* had slipped ahead. Walter was not having that. He slipped anchor, edged his way forward between them, and swung his ship broadside across the channel so that no one could pass ahead of him.

"Look, sir," shouted a seaman a few minutes later, "the *Nonpareil's* gone and fastened a rope to our side–they're reckoning to pull themselves up level with us."

"Impudence!" said Walter. "Cut the rope."

It was done. The *Nonpareil* fell back into place, all but her bows masked from even a view of the enemy. Even in that desperate moment Walter saw the humor of the situation, for in the *Nonpareil* was the Lord Admiral himself, who had left his flagship in safety and insisted on taking a personal share in the battle.

The flyboats would not come now. They had been seen, but they had fouled each other in the crowded channel. He must risk the *Warspite* herself. He gave orders to warp alongside and prepare for boarding.

But the enemy did not wait. They ran the galleon aground and set her on fire. It was a hideous spectacle, with helpless men tumbling out of her hull like coals from a sack, to drown or be butchered as they swam by the Dutchmen, who now put out in boats to make their first real contribution to the battle. Walter, his lip curling with disgust, drove them off as well as he could, and soon he was joined in that work of mercy by the Lord Admiral.

The battle was going splendidly. The *Saint Thomas* also had gone up in flames, but two other galleons had been captured intact. The sea fight was entering its last phase.

Suddenly Walter felt an agonizing blow on the leg and collapsed, streaming with blood, upon the deck.

It was a serious wound. His leg was stabbed with jagged splinters, and, as it turned out, he was never to walk without a limp again.

But he set his teeth, determined not to be left out of the fighting that lay ahead. Essex was landing troops. He insisted on going ashore himself, carried on men's shoulders. A horse was brought. They lifted him into the saddle, but the agony was unbearable. He went back to his ship.

All night he lay in pain, his mind working desperately. It was maddening to be laid low like this at a time when such golden opportunities were dangled before the expedition. Could the elderly Lord Admiral be relied upon to seize them? Would Essex be sensible or follow some wild scheme of his own? Above all—what about the West Indian convoy, lying helpless in Puerto Real, a prize worth twelve million crowns ready for the taking?

At dawn he sent his half-brother, Sir John Gilbert, to visit the supreme commanders. Young Arthur

Throckmorton went with him. They were to ask permission on Walter's behalf to move in and seize the convoy.

They came back helpless and exasperated. They had found the commanders stunned by the ease of their own victory. Cadiz town had fallen the night before. This morning the Lord Admiral had just received the surrender of Fort Puntal, and the Castle had lowered its flag to Essex. They were now so busy arranging ransoms and restoring order in the town that they could spare no thoughts for the prizes awaiting them across the bay.

Walter lay fuming. During that day there came a message that the merchants of Spain offered a ransom of two million ducats for their ships and cargoes. "Seize the ships first, and bargain afterward," Walter advised, but no decision was made that day.

It was the Duke of Medina Sidonia, the Spanish commander, who decided the question. The next morning Arthur came rushing into Walter's cabin, almost weeping with fury and disappointment.

"It's burning!"

"What's burning?"

"The West Indian convoy! The Spaniards have set it on fire—you can see a great smoke cloud over Puerto Real."

"The fools!" groaned Walter. And he did not mean the Spaniards.

They got home in August. They had something to show for the expedition, but they might have had so much more. If Walter blamed Essex for losing the westbound convoy, Essex could retort that they had also missed a homeward-bound treasure fleet which had anchored in Lisbon two days after their departure —all because Howard and Raleigh said the navy was in no fit condition to hang about any longer.

It was easy to be wise after the event, thought Walter. No one had known at the time that another day or two would have given them the treasure.

Both of them had a surprise on landing. Robert Cecil, third rival for the Queen's favor, had taken advantage of their absence to get himself made Secretary of State. Essex was angry; he had meant to work one of his followers, Thomas Bodley, into the post. Walter cared less. Cecil, crafty and cold-blooded as he was, had never done him any real harm—he passed for a friend of the family, if he could be said to feel anything as warm as friendship. Neither Walter nor Essex got much credit for Cadiz, so far as the Queen was concerned. Most people considered him the hero of the sea fight, but she had no thanks for him.

Fortunately, it suited Cecil to do him a good turn. He worked on her by degrees, dropping a sly word here and another there. On the first of June, the anniversary of the departure for Cadiz, Walter was summoned to the Queen's presence.

It was five years since they had met. She had aged greatly. Her face had thinned, she had lost many of her teeth, and what she had were yellow. She was as vividly dressed as ever, in silver gauze and crimson, with slashed sleeves lined with red taffeta, and a great many pearls and rubies. When she stood up and moved vigorously across the room, he saw that she had lost none of her old grace and dignity.

"Well, Water?" Her reddened lips crinkled, the nickname came strangely sounding, and it was only as she went on that he realized how the loss of teeth had altered her voice. "So you've returned to duty? Henceforth let me see you at your post in the Privy Chamber! What's the use of a Captain of the Guard who's never there?" She plucked at the open neck of her gown as though she were hot. "Come, it's too fine a day to be indoors. It's a long time since we had a ride together."

CHAPTER XI

The Voyage to the Islands

THE QUEEN soon had other work for him. Walter knew he would never get back all her old favor. He might ride with her, talk with her, stand guard at the door of her Privy Chamber, but she could do without him and would send him away if need arose.

That suited him. To be only a courtier, tied (so to speak) to the royal apron strings, led nowhere. He must be free to move, to cross the Atlantic and revisit Guiana, to see Virginia. . . . But he must also have power and influence. He must be able to see the Queen whenever he needed to, he must know what was going on around the throne, who would help forward his dreams of colonization and empire, who would block them. . . .

Court—and colonies! It was like trying to ride two spirited horses at once, a foot on each. A dangerous game. You could not afford to fall.

Within a fortnight of Walter's return to favor he

was named Rear-Admiral again in another expedition against the Spaniards. It was very much like last year's fleet, with most of the same officers—Cousin George was sailing this time in the galleon *Saint Matthew*, captured at Cadiz—and the usual dandified crowd of gentlemen volunteers. There was one important difference: Essex was appointed supreme commander, and old Lord Howard was to serve under him as Vice-Admiral.

This time the objective was Ferrol, the base on the northern coast of Spain, where King Philip was known to be massing another armada for the invasion of England.

Walter grew impatient with this position—the Spaniards were *always* preparing the invasion of England. One of these fine days they would manage to land an army (not even England should rely on bad weather to protect her forever), and then let the Queen look out. Whatever they were like on the water, the Dons were the finest soldiers in Europe. They would go through England like a knife through butter.

The Queen should spend her money on one terrific knockdown blow and wipe out the menace for good and all. That was all very well, Cecil told him with a faint smile—he was like all the commanders, always blaming her meanness and economy. The Queen had her reasons; she had to keep the whole country going, not only her soldiers and sailors, but judges, officials, ambassadors, secret agents, people of every sort. Englishmen hated to pay taxes, so she must find what income she could and, like a careful housewife, stretch it as far as possible. She was not like Philip, receiving a convoy of gold and silver every year from America. In fact, the effect of all that gold and silver pouring into Europe was to make her own money worth less and double her difficulties.

Walter said no more. The subject of treasure fleets was painful.

They sailed in July. The Queen provided twenty ships, the Dutch ten. All the other ninety vessels were privately owned, sailing in hopes of plunder.

They ran straight into a furious storm which battered them for several days. Walter was in the *Warspite* again, and at one time gave himself up for lost. The wind screamed and whined about the bare masts, for the sails were torn from the yards as soon as they were spread. Huge waves crashed against the sides, and the ship rolled over so far that he wondered if she would ever right herself. The cook's galley, built of bricks as a safeguard against fire, was almost shaken to pieces. The beams groaned and creaked with every blow. He found himself wondering which would happen first: would she break up, or would she capsize, top-heavy with bad construction and overloaded with heavy guns? If he lived he would have something to say to these shipbuilders, with their mania for floating castles. . . .

He lived, but he was driven back to Plymouth. So were Essex and most of the others. Some of the gentlemen volunteers had died from exhaustion and prolonged sickness. Others, having had enough of the adventure, landed and went home.

It was a month before they got off again, and the day was then so calm that they had to be towed as far as the open sea. The fine weather did not last long. Another storm struck them in the Bay of Biscay. The *Saint Matthew* lost her foremast, and George had to turn for home. Walter never undressed or lay in his cabin for ten days. At last, when his main yard had been carried away, he was forced to fire a gun as a signal of distress. Essex sailed up and cheerfully announced that his own ship was leaking as desperately as a ship could without actually sinking. He fixed a meeting place and bore away. In such weather it was every ship for herself.

They met again off Flores, most westerly island of the Azores. The raid on Ferrol had been given up. Their latest information was that the Spanish Admiral was not sailing against England after all; instead, he had put out to meet the treasure fleet from America. As this fleet always came in by way of the Azores—a welcome stopping place for fresh water and provisions—Essex decided to lay an ambush there.

Walter was glad enough to call at Flores, for his water supply was dangerously low. He asked Essex for leave to take on water, and started the work. It took time—there were hundreds of heavy casks to go ashore, to be trundled along the beach, heaved into the boats again, and hoisted aboard in slings. Luckily the islanders were friendly. Looting was forbidden, the English were paying for all they took, and there were plenty of tender young chickens, oranges, and grapes to be had.

Suddenly, in the very middle of this, Essex sent a curt order. He was to stop what he was doing, weigh anchor and follow immediately to Fayal, the next island to the east. Walter raised his eyebrows, but obeyed as quickly as he could. The men came tumbling back, sail was spread, and one by one the ships in the squadron stood out to sea.

They sighted Fayal next day—but not the Earl.

He and his fleet had vanished as completely as though the Atlantic had swallowed them up, which, considering the fineness of the weather, was mysterious, to say the least of it.

For three days Walter lay off the town of Horta, nestling white and yellow against the vineyards and wooded mountainsides. For three days he watched the garrison strengthening its defenses and the townsfolk evacuating their valuables inland.

"It's maddening," he told Kemys. "We could have taken Horta the day we arrived—but you know how touchy Essex is! *He* wants the glory. If we attack without him he'll be furious."

That third day the fort hoisted a red flag of defiance and opened fire on the anchored squadron. This was more than Walter could bear. He summoned a council of war.

Most of the officers begged him to attack. The Portuguese must not think him afraid. . . . Some went so far as to hint that he was.

Only Sir Gilly Merrick and Sir Christopher Blount, two of the Earl's toadies, insisted that he should wait. When the decision went against them, they stood aside and said their half-dozen ships would take no part.

Walter was not worried, for he could do very

well without them. He picked five hundred men: sailors, with a few gentlemen volunteers he could not refuse, but no soldiers, as he felt they belonged to the Earl. Then, ignoring Sir Gilly and his party, he sailed the rest of his squadron around a headland and anchored off a beach four miles to the south of Horta.

Essex had told him to leave off watering at Flores; he could water at Fayal. Very well. Essex could hardly complain if, after waiting so long, he now went ahead to get the water he needed. If, of course, the enemy prevented his doing so he would be compelled to fight back. . . .

"Very ingenious," commented Kemys with a smile. He eyed the coast. "It won't be too easy."

"Oh, as for that . . . the working of the sea and the steepness of the cliffs—*they're* nothing new to our fellows. Quite like Devon! But, look, there are some troops marching down from the headland. . . . They're entrenching themselves on the beach." Walter chuckled. "I'm very much afraid, Laurence, we shall be forced to defend ourselves."

He ordered the first half of his volunteers to the boats. He went with them, staff in hand to help his limp, as casually as though he were going ashore on a pleasure excursion. He was dressed as gaily as usual, in doublet and full-cut breeches, with a spotless white sash. His helmet and breastplate went into the boat, but he did not put them on. Kemys and Cousin Arthur Gorges went with him.

The rowers pushed off, the boats made for the shore, climbing and diving over the glassy rollers, nearer and nearer to where the sea boiled soapily around the reef. Suddenly there was a crackle of musketry, splinters flew from the gunwale, and several men collapsed over their oars. The boats wavered in their onward rush. These men were sailors, not soldiers: brave enough in face of their own dangers, but not used to small-arms fire.

Walter stood up, a conspicuous target, and bawled furiously in his broad Devon. Those who were afraid could turn back. The rest should follow him and get on with it. He shouted this in the vigorous but unprintable language which sailors best understand on such occasions. They answered by bending to their oars again. The boats shot forward so recklessly that several were damaged as they bumped the reef. Yelling like demons and jumping over the rocks like goats, the landing party grappled with the defenders. For a moment there was a fierce tussle. Pistols snapped, cutlass clashed against pike. By the time Walter got there, hampered as he was by his game leg, the Portuguese had bolted and the beach was won.

"Now what?" panted Kemys.

"I'm sending the boats back for more men. Then the town." Walter studied the ground. "We shall be under fire from the fort. We must make for that group of tors; they'll give us cover."

The reinforcements arrived, formed up on the beach, and marched off in military formation. The forty gentlemen volunteers led the way with Walter at their head, leaning heavily on a stick. A hot fire swept their line of march, and the men very sensibly broke ranks and raced for the shelter of the crags in front. But Walter never quickened his leisurely, disdainful pace, and the gentlemen behind him did not dare to duck and run. Everyone was heartily glad to reach cover.

"Now, gentlemen, we must reconnoiter the way forward to the town. Can I have volunteers, please?"

There was no answer. Everyone had been a little shaken, and no one was in a hurry to quit the sheltering rocks. There was a stiff climb in front, exposed to the enemy sharpshooters.

"Very well," said Walter, without moving a muscle to show his feelings, "I'll go myself."

"No!" burst out Kemys. "You mustn't, sir–it's too dangerous."

"Nonsense. Where's my helmet? Thanks. Give me a hand with this breastplate. You can come with me, if you like, Laurence."

Kemys did. So did Arthur and half a dozen others. As soon as they showed themselves in the sunshine again the musketry sputtered from the fort, and bullets went screeching among the boulders.

Walter turned to his cousin. "It's that confounded red sash of yours!" he shouted. "Talk about a red rag to a bull! You'd better take it off."

Arthur grinned. "What about your white one?"

"Oh . . . hang it! All right, keep it on. Can't let the Dons dictate what we wear."

They scrambled on. A few moments later Arthur let out a cry of pain. A musket ball had struck him in the leg. They helped him forward and reached a place from which they could scan the approaches to the town. Walter decided on his plan and sent back word to the main party. They advanced to the assault, only to find that the garrison had fled from the town and sought shelter in the fort.

"We'll deal with them tomorrow," said Walter contentedly. "Meanwhile we've got Horta cheaply enough." He looked down at his breeches and realized for the first time that they were slashed with bullet holes. "Not so cheaply as I'd thought," he added with a smile. "It was lucky they were cut on the full side."

Before he could tackle the fort next morning, word came that the *Due Repulse* and the rest of the fleet had been sighted. Walter felt vexed. As Essex had been so late, what a pity he could not have been a few hours later! He would have liked to finish the job, but knew the young Earl too well to do anything so foolish. The only thing to do was to go back to the *Warspite*, pick up the barge he used for formal visits, and report to his commander on the flagship. Essex would surely be pleased that everything had gone off so well. There was still the fort to be captured, and he was welcome to land his soldiers and win the glory of that.

When he was shown into the Earl's cabin he saw at once that there was something wrong. Essex's look was black as a thundercloud, and all the officers looked grim. Sir Gilly was there, and Sir Christopher. . . . Was that it? They'd run straight to their master and tried to make trouble.

"So you got my order to report here?" Essex

spoke in a cold tone, his temper under doubtful control.

"Order?" Walter looked blank. "I've had no order, my lord. But I heard you had arrived, and naturally I came at once to tell you the position and guide you to the lines opposite the fort."

"Why did you dare to land without my permission? You know the standing order—no troops to be landed at any time except at my direction."

"Yes, my lord, of course, but—"

"Do you realize, Sir Walter, that I have power to form a court-martial of these gentlemen present here now, to sentence you to death and execute you? Without reference to anyone in England!"

Walter stood silent for a moment, surveying the company with his heavy-lidded eyes. He was in a dangerous situation. Some of these men hated him. They were the Earl's men, they owed their careers to Essex—even their knighthoods. He had never hidden his contempt for them, and this was their chance. Essex was different. There was much to admire in Essex himself, and in spite of their rivalry they had often found it possible to work together. But now Essex was in one of his moods. His conceit was pricked. Egged on by his toadies, Essex was capable of anything.

"If you'll allow me to defend myself," he said very quietly, "I think it will appear that I have committed no fault."

"How? The rule is clear."

"If you will glance at those orders again, my lord —I know them, for I helped to word them—you will see that '*No captain of a ship or company shall land without direction.*' Now I take myself to be a principal commander in this fleet—in the absence of your lordship and Lord Howard I take over command. So, as a principal commander, I cannot be court-martialed."

"H'm." Essex tugged his square beard doubtfully. He could not answer that point for the moment.

Walter pressed his advantage. "Besides, my lord, you agreed I should land here—"

"With me!"

"I waited four days. As you did not arrive, my lord—though you had twenty miles start of me—I concluded you thought me strong enough to carry it out alone."

Essex flushed angrily. "I turned aside to look for the treasure fleet."

"If your lordship had thought fit to tell me. . . ." Walter stopped, with a polite but ever so faintly mocking gesture.

Essex blustered for some time after that, but he knew, and Walter knew, that there was no case for a court-martial. All the same, Walter was glad to get safely away to the billet he had taken as his headquarters in the town. Essex was capable of taking chances and making his own rules, relying on his charm to twist the Queen around his little finger and make everything all right afterward.

No move was made against the fort that day. In the morning Lord Howard came to see Walter. Walter had made up his mind by now—he would not put himself in Essex's power again. If Essex summoned him to a court-martial, he would take his whole squadron and sail away. If Essex tried to stop him, he would have to fight a sea battle.

"Stuff!" said the old Admiral. "You go and apologize to Essex and that'll end the matter."

"It'll end *my* matter if he whips my head off."

"I've spoken to Essex. You can trust me, Sir Walter. I give you my word of honor, no harm shall be done to you."

That meant something. Walter respected Lord Howard, and so (he knew) did Essex. He put on his best clothes (Essex of late had grown positively slovenly in his dress and needed showing up) and waited upon his rival. The apology was formal, stiff, and insincere, but it had to be made. It was accepted.

"And now," said the Earl with dignity, "I shall proceed to take the fort."

He sent off a force to cut the garrison's line of retreat and then summoned them to surrender. To this they made no reply, for the very good reason that they had all escaped into the hills during the night. The fort which Essex entered contained only two men, and both of them had been dead for some time.

Altogether, apart from Walter's capture of Horta, the whole expedition was a distinct failure.

Hearing that the treasure fleet was approaching, Essex threw out a positive net of ships, into which it would most certainly have sailed had he not changed his dispositions at the last moment. As a result the treasure fleet sailed blithely into port only three hours after its course was left clear. On another occasion Walter was within an ace of capturing a rich galleon of eighteen hundred tons, but lost it through the disobedience of a Dutch captain and had to watch its priceless cargo of sugar and spices go up in flames.

Worst of all, when they got back to Plymouth they found that the Spanish invasion fleet had, after all, sailed from Ferrol. England had been in panic, with her navy far away cruising among the Azores. Bad weather, not guns, had scattered the enemy and driven them home.

The Queen was in no welcoming mood.

C H A P T E R X I I

Treason and Plot

MATTERS WERE SMOOTHED OVER. Elizabeth was old, too old to train new men for her service. Essex, with all his faults, must be forgiven. "Water" had served her well on the whole. He should remain in favor, and perhaps even be promoted.

Walter was not so well nowadays. His wounded leg troubled him at times. He went more often to Bath to take the waters. But his mind was as alert as ever.

There was whispering that he would be made an earl, a Privy Councilor, even Vice-Chamberlain, and that Bess would be forgiven and recalled to Court. All that came to nothing. He could certainly have been Lord Deputy of Ireland, but he refused. He had no desire to go back there. There had been a rising—Kilcolman Castle, like many another, had been sacked by the rebels and his friend Spenser driven into penniless exile, where he had died brokenhearted. Walter wanted no more to do with that unhappy country. He sold his estates there, except for the castle of Inchiquin Raleigh, which he had let to Katharine, Dowager Countess of Desmond, as long as she lived. As this lady claimed to have been born in 1464 it seemed unlikely that she would live much longer. In actual fact she survived until 1604, being then (if her birth date was accurate) one hundred and forty years old. Even then, gossip said, her death was an accident: she had fallen from an apple tree while climbing to pick the fruit.

Essex would have liked the office of Lord Deputy for another man. When the Queen rejected his idea he lost his temper and turned his back on her. Elizabeth, too, could lose her temper.

"Go and be hanged!" she shouted, and gave him a terrific clout on the ear.

Essex spun around, face flaming as red as his ear, and reached for his sword. "I wouldn't have stood that from your father Henry!" he cried chokingly. "I won't stand it from a–a king in petticoats!"

Courtiers hustled him away before he could, in two senses, lose his head.

There was trouble that year at the Queen's birthday festivities, when a magnificent tournament was held. Walter planned to bring his small train of followers in new livery, with orange plumes in their hats. Essex heard of it and turned up with two thousand men in the same colors. Elizabeth showed him plainly what she thought of this vulgar and snobbish action. Some day, she meditated wearily, she must deal with this cocksure young Earl. . . . But she felt old and tired, she had always loved him in spite of his behavior. . . . Also, for some reason, Essex was the darling of the London crowd, while "Water" was hated. And a man who could gather two thousand followers for a birthday tournament must be handled with care.

Walter was working (as he said himself) like a mule. In London he was speaking regularly in Parliament. Apart from his usual Court duties he was often asked to look after foreign statesmen when they visited England–few other men had the necessary command of modern languages. He found time not only to keep up his old friendships with writers and scientists, but to found a club at the Mermaid Tavern, where he could talk with such men as Ben Jonson and that Shakespeare who had satirized him a few years before.

In the West Country he still had much business: he was responsible for coast defenses, for the tin-mining industry and other matters. He had his finger in shipping ventures and colonization schemes. He was the first man to import mahogany to England.

At home in Sherborne he was still beautifying the castle and its grounds. The Virginia cedars had arrived and were planted. Will Cecil, delicate son of the Queen's Secretary, spent long holidays at the castle and grew fitter in the healthy country air. His own son, Wat, was breeched, and a proper little man.

As if these affairs did not keep him sufficiently occupied, the Queen made him Governor of Jersey, in the Channel Islands. Bess and Wat accompanied him to Weymouth on a fine October day and saw him off. Winds were contrary, and the short sea passage took two days and nights. He was royally entertained on landing and thought Jersey as pleasant an island as he had ever seen. The post proved worth barely a third of the salary he had been promised. Nevertheless, he did his duty well, strengthened the defenses, helped the people to develop trade with Newfoundland, and stopped a system of compulsory service which had been highly unpopular. Then, having a hundred and one other responsibilities, he returned to England.

Treason and Plot

How long would the old Queen last?

That question was in everyone's mind and on nobody's lips. To discuss her death was practically treason, yet die she must, being human. Who would succeed her? She would never say. It was more and more obvious that, unless something unforeseen happened, it would be King James of Scotland, her cousin, and son of that cousin Mary Stuart she had put to death.

Unless something unforeseen happened . . .

While a man like the Earl of Essex was alive one never knew. He had missed his chance (many said) to become the Queen's husband years ago. But he was still young, and there seemed no limit to his vanity and to his ambition. There was no knowing what he would do.

The Queen packed him off to Ireland as commander-in-chief against Tyrone's rebels, yet there were some who felt he might prove more dangerous over there, with an army, than at home without one. Once there was a scare that he was coming back at the head of his troops, and for a whole fortnight London was barricaded.

But Essex, when he came, returned quickly and secretly, leaving his forces in Ireland and his work there undone. He rode furiously to London with a few friends, changed horses, and thundered on through the September dawn to Nonesuch, where the Queen was staying.

No one knew he was coming. The Queen was just up, sitting at her dressing table with her hair down and no make-up on her face. Essex flung himself from the saddle, rushed through the outer rooms and burst in upon her, himself filthy from the mud of the road. No other man alive would have dared so much.

She stared at him, unable for a moment to believe her eyes.

"God's death, my lord!" she swore. "What are you doing here, your presence hateful, without Tyrone's head?"

He knelt to kiss her hand. "I have made a truce with Tyrone–"

"A truce with a rebel? Is this how you obey my orders? When I absolutely commanded you, on your allegiance, you should not presume to come over without my permission!"

"*Presume*, madam?"

"That was my word. And now you *presume* to burst in upon me like this! Get out!"

Like a fury she drove him out. But within an hour

she had sent for him again, talked with him until midday about Ireland, and seemed to have forgiven him.

It looked as though "the great boy" had done it again. He swaggered into dinner and was quickly surrounded by friends. Walter and Cecil, sitting at a table apart with several others, got only a distant and chilly greeting from him.

But it proved that Essex had banked on his charm once too often. Elizabeth veered again like the weathercock she was. Late in the evening he was ordered to stay in his room. Three days later he was sent to London, to remain at York House under honorable arrest. He remained there for nearly a year. Then he was released, but forbidden to appear at Court. After a few days at his town house off the Strand, he left for his uncle's home in Oxfordshire, announcing that he proposed to live a quiet country life.

Walter wondered. True, his old rival had been ill, and was far from healthy even now. But he had a feeling that England had not heard the last of Essex.

The Earl had turned his eyes north to the King of Scotland. It would pay him best, he decided, to befriend James, so that he would become his right-hand man when James succeeded to the English throne. As soon he must, either on the Queen's death –or earlier.

Or earlier . . .

He had returned to London. Essex House was once more a great center of society. He was surrounded by soldiers of fortune and adventurers of all kinds. He maintained his own spies and agents both at home and abroad. Around his neck he wore a small black bag, next the skin. It contained a note of seven lines, but highly important lines, from James Stuart.

On a Saturday afternoon in February, 1601, there was a performance by special request of Shakespeare's *Richard II* at the Globe. The company had not wished to put on the play, which was old. Certain friends of Essex persuaded them by offering a sum of money to increase the box-office takings. The audience was full of Essex supporters, including Sir Gilly Merrick and Sir Christopher Blount, with whom Walter had had such trouble during the attack on Fayal.

It was plain to all why *Richard II* had been asked for: it was the story of an English sovereign who had been put off the throne to make room for another. The Earl was popular with the Londoners.

The play would remind them of what had happened once before, and might happen again.

It was an anxious week end for Walter, who, as Captain of the Guard, was particularly responsible for the Queen's safety. Revolution might break out at any moment. The Queen was at Whitehall and there were no troops to defend her, only the gentlemen of the Guard and the palace servants; Essex House, a bare mile away along the Strand, was an armed camp, with the Earl's supporters flocking in from the country every hour. Needless to say, it was waste of breath suggesting to the Queen that she should move to a safer place.

Even Sir Ferdinando Gorges, one of his own relatives, had left his post as Governor of Plymouth Fort and arrived at Essex House. That showed which way the wind was blowing. As the fort came under Walter's command as Vice-Admiral of the West, Gorges was in a sense under his orders. He sent word asking him to come to Durham House and explain why he had deserted his post.

Gorges refused to enter Durham House—so it had come to that!—but agreed to a meeting by boat in mid-river. They met, and Walter tried to reason with him.

"You know," he said, "if you don't go back to

Plymouth you may find yourself in the Fleet Prison."

Gorges scoffed at the idea. "This is no time to talk of the fleet, Sir Walter. You get back to Court, and speedily! Essex has put a strong guard around his house, and you'll likely have a bloody day of it."

They parted. As Walter's boat moved back to his private landing steps, Sir Christopher Blount appeared in another craft and fired four times at him with a musket, but without hitting him.

Things moved quickly that Sunday. A party of important officials was sent to Essex House, calling on the Earl to submit himself in the Queen's name. Encouraged by his friends and the cheering mob outside, he put them under arrest in his own study, leaving three musketeers on guard at the door with lighted matches, ready to shoot. With his chief followers he discussed plans to seize the Court, the Tower, and the City of London.

Meanwhile, Walter and the Queen's Council were making frenzied preparations. Elizabeth would not budge from Whitehall. She carried on with her day's program unaltered, not a hint of alarm upon her sharp old face. As she sat at dinner the news came that Essex had started to march through the City, bidding the people arm and join him. He was being cheered on all sides. . . .

"He Who placed me on this throne will preserve me on it," she said calmly, and picked up another chicken bone.

Walter, who had so often suffered from her temper, could not help but love her for her courage. He had little time to think of himself, though one thing was plain: if Essex succeeded, he himself was as good as dead.

They had collected all the arms they could. The trainbands of Westminster, Chelsea, and the surrounding villages had been summoned. A barricade of coaches had been chained wheel to wheel across the wide road leading from Charing Cross.

By the afternoon Essex still had not moved against them. They had collected three companies of infantry and a few dozen horsemen. It was all they could do to persuade the Queen from leading them against the rebels herself. She saw nothing strange in such a Sunday afternoon excursion for an old lady verging on seventy.

Essex bungled this last warlike operation as he had bungled others in his career. He waited too long, and he relied on the support of Londoners who were not prepared to do more than shout from the safety of upstairs windows. He could always draw their cheers, but he could not draw their swords.

There was a skirmish at Ludgate, a brief siege of Essex House, and a scuffle in the courtyard. That same night, before the cannon brought from the Tower had begun to bombard the walls, Essex and his followers came out into the torchlight, knelt, and surrendered their swords.

It was all over. The clocks in the City struck eleven.

Ten days later Essex was tried in Westminster Hall on a charge of "conspiring to deprive and depose the Queen's Majesty from her royal state and dignity, and to procure her death and destruction."

Walter was called as a witness. His evidence was not important—he merely reported his meeting with Gorges on the river—but Essex scowled at him as though the whole case was his doing. When Walter stood up to take the oath, he burst out scornfully:

"What is the use of swearing that fox? That small Testament won't make him tell the truth—give him a big folio Bible!"

There was ample other evidence against him, though he had thrown his mysterious black bag into the fire before his surrender. Like Sir Christopher

Blount and several of his other followers (though not many, for the Queen proved merciful), he was sentenced to death.

As Captain of the Guard, Walter had to attend all such executions. Blount, on the scaffold, asked, "Is Sir Walter Raleigh here?"

Walter stepped forward. "Here I am, Sir Christopher."

"I thank God you are present. I had an infinite desire to speak to you, to ask your forgiveness, before I died."

"I most willingly forgive you," said Walter quietly, "and I beseech God to forgive you—and to give you His divine comfort." He turned earnestly to the spectators and said, "I protest before God that, whatever Sir Christopher Blount meant toward me, I for my part never bore him any evil intention."

A little later, when Blount was asked to cut short his last messages, he interfered with a protest. Surely a dying man should be allowed the few minutes he needed?

When the turn of Essex came, he stood close to the scaffold, hoping that the Earl, too, would make peace with him before the ax fell. They had had bitter rivalries and quarrels, but they had also served together in war and council. Then he heard a whisper among the crowd:

"Look at that fox Raleigh—come to gloat over his enemy!"

He winced. Duty compelled him to watch the execution, but he moved into the Armory, where he could see, unseen, from the window. There was no look of gloating on his face, but a shadow of great sadness.

Essex stripped off his black satin doublet and knelt down, a vivid figure in a scarlet waistcoat. The ax rose and came down.

Not until later did Walter learn that Essex had asked for him in those last minutes, to make peace with him. "Sir Walter," he had declared to the bystanders, "is a true servant to the Queen and the State—I know nothing otherwise."

Nonetheless, many people continued to regard Walter as a cunning schemer who had lured the Earl to his death.

It would have been better for Walter if he had shown a little of the cunning he was supposed to possess. He might then have thought of his own future, served the Queen less, and the King of Scotland more.

The real fox was Robert Cecil, the humpbacked Secretary. Outwardly he was an old family friend—had he not sent his boy to spend long country holidays at Sherborne? In reality, he was a rival more dangerous than Essex had ever been.

Cecil was determined that when the new King came there should be no rivalry around the throne. He would be supreme. Essex was dead. That was extraordinarily lucky; who would have believed that the Queen could have brought herself to sign the warrant? Walter would not be so obliging as to play the fool that way. He must be put out of the running in some other way.

For some time Cecil had been writing regularly to the Scots King. The correspondence was strictly secret. Persons were mentioned not by names but by numbers. There was a key to the code:

Raleigh	2
Howard	3
Cecil	10
The Queen	24
The King	30

He had a nervous moment once when driving with the Queen in her coach. They met the courier from Scotland, and she asked for the mail. He knew there was a letter in the bag which, if she saw it, would mean his ruin. He hurried back to the coach as though eager to put the bag in her hands, calling for a knife to cut the fastenings. Then suddenly he pulled a face and sniffed.

"Madam, the bag is dirty–it smells!"

He gambled on her delicate nose, and won. "The letters can wait," she said. "Drive on."

In this correspondence with James he managed to poison the King's mind, drop by drop, against Walter. It was all very skillfully done.

Walter, meantime, had no notion that Cecil was anything but his old friend. Cecil continued as his partner in various shipping ventures, drawing handsome profits. Business after all was business, the sly little man believed.

CHAPTER XIII

The Shadow of the Scaffold

So SHE WAS DEAD AT LAST.

In his hands he held the letter from the Privy Council calling him to London. The messenger must have shouted his news to the town as he came, for, listen! the bells were beginning to toll for the passing of the Queen.

It was no surprise, for she had been failing all through that winter of 1603, and now, before the first dawn light of an early spring day, she had gone. Elizabeth, by the Grace of God, of England, France, and Ireland Queen, Defender of the Faith . . . Gloriana, the Faerie Queen, Cynthia (as he had called her in his own poem) . . . the strange woman who had ruled England ever since he could remember . . . was dead. It would take time to get used to the idea.

She had been mean, jealous, unfair, and vain. All that was true. But she had also been gay and witty, warmhearted and affectionate, tireless to serve her people, and never in the grimmest danger afraid.

So, with all her faults, she had been great, glorious, and—dearly loved. She had been human. Could James of Scotland be called human? Walter remembered reports he had heard and smiled wryly. James might be a learned scholar, a powerful writer, shrewd—but he looked and behaved like a clown.

Was it still too late to save England from such a king? And from the Scotsmen who (thought Walter, disliking them) would come swarming southward like locusts to seize all the posts and offices they could? He must see what they were saying in London.

He posted eastward at top speed to obey the summons of the Privy Council. They had already proclaimed the new King. They were now drawing up a message of welcome, which they wanted signed by as many leading men as possible.

Walter looked round at the faces in the room. Here were the ablest statesmen in England, none of them angels, but probably the worst of them more of a man than this James Stuart. There was something absurd in such men going down on bended knees to offer the crown to him.

And all because he had been Elizabeth's second cousin!

He thought of the ancient Athenians and the glory they had won—without a king. He remembered that Rome's noblest days had been when she was a republic. From more modern times he recalled the examples of Florence, Venice, and the Netherlands.

"Let's keep the staff in our own hands," he suggested boldly, "and set up a commonwealth. We don't want to be subject to a needy, beggarly nation like the Scots."

There was a shocked silence. Men exchanged glances. Most of them were thinking not of England's future but of their own. They did not wish to offend their new master in any way.

Walter made a more moderate suggestion, which was backed by his friend Lord Cobham and a few others. James should be king only on terms. He must, for instance, limit the number of Scotsmen he brought into England with him.

That idea also was turned down. Those who knew James best knew that he believed passionately in the divine right of kings. Kings (in his own view) were appointed by God and were above the laws of man.

So he would certainly not bargain with his future subjects.

Walter did not press the matter. It seemed a pity to let England go so cheap, but for himself he was not worried. He knew his own value, and he knew that, with Drake and all the other old commanders dead, he was the most able Englishman alive in his own line. James would need all the good men he could find.

He therefore did not join in the undignified rush to meet James on his journey southward and to curry favor from the start. However, common sense warned him not to be too casual, so, making the best of a bad job, he rode to Burghley House and met the King as he drew near the capital.

He had a cold welcome. James looked at him with shifty, rolling eyes, his large tongue lolling from his mouth.

"Rawly? Rawly?" he said when Walter's name was announced, and added with a snigger, "Aye, true enough, for I think of ye verra rawly, mon."

Walter looked gravely at him and hoped that his own contempt and disgust would not show in his face. James was all that had been described, and worse.

He was fat and looked fatter because of his

stuffed and baggy clothes. He was terrified of being murdered and could not bear to see a naked sword: breeches and doublet alike were heavily quilted to make them daggerproof. He had a mean thin beard, and his skin—well, Walter had no longer any difficulty in believing that James never washed. His clothes would have disgraced any man, let alone a king. He looked as though he had slept in them not the night before but for years, and it was not difficult to guess what dishes he had taken at recent meals.

He seemed equally unable to sit still for long or to stand up straight by himself. He preferred to lean on someone, or to waddle unsteadily around the room, plucking and fumbling with his fingers.

They talked for a time. James promised that he should continue Lieutenant of Cornwall and Lord Warden of the Stannaries. It was clear that James was vastly enjoying his new power. He had already, at Newark on the way down, hanged a thief without trial, to show that he was above the law. He boasted now to Walter that, if it had been necessary, he would have taken the English throne by force of arms.

"Would God that had been put to the trial!" Walter retorted swiftly, looking down at this King who could not bear to see, let alone use, a sword. He had once, when conferring a knighthood, nearly poked out the eye of the kneeling courtier, because his nervous gaze had roved away from what he was doing.

"Why?" demanded James.

"Because Your Majesty would then have known your friends from your foes."

And he left James to work that out.

James went on thinking, and his thoughts about Walter grew no pleasanter.

Walter was a fighting man; James detested all fighting men. Indeed, he detested almost everything about Walter, even to his tobacco smoking. Was it not Walter who had introduced to Britain this "*custom loathsome to the eye, hateful to the nose, harmful to the brain, dangerous to the lungs, and in the black stinking fume thereof nearest resembling the horrible Stygian smoke of the pit that is bottomless . . .*"? James was already framing the violent pamphlet against smokers he was to publish the following year.

James thought, then acted. Walter found himself no longer Captain of the Guard; a Scot was put in his place. He was given sudden notice to turn out of Durham House, which had been his London home for nearly twenty years, and on which he had spent two thousand pounds of his own money in repairs.

Then one July morning, as he waited on the terrace at Windsor, dressed to ride with the King to a stag hunt, Cecil came out to him, his face a mask of politeness.

"Oh, Sir Walter, you aren't to go with the King this morning."

"But I have his orders–"

"This is another order–as from the King. You're wanted in the Council Chamber. The Privy Council have some questions to ask you."

What fresh irritation now? Walter was faintly but not seriously worried as he turned and followed the little Secretary along the terrace. He did not know that he had started on the walk which would lead him to the foot of the scaffold.

There had been plots against the King already, but Walter knew no more of them than he knew of the Gunpowder Plot, which was still to come. He had an inkling that his friend Lord Cobham kept up a connection with the Spanish Minister in the Netherlands, but that was all. Lately he had seen less of Cobham anyhow, but for old times' sake he had not dropped the friendship altogether.

Now, to his horrified amazement, he found himself suspected of joining in a plot with Cobham and —of all people—his lifelong enemies the Spaniards! Nothing could have been more laughable if it had not also been a matter of life and death.

He was at first put under house arrest, then sent to the Tower. Day after day he was questioned and cross-questioned. Kemys, as his close friend, was seized as a witness and threatened with torture, but he would say nothing against Walter, for there was nothing to be said. Lord Cobham, however, who had never had much nerve, lost what he had: believing that Walter had accused him, he turned around and accused Walter. The prisoners were not allowed to communicate, but Walter managed to send Cobham a letter concealed in an apple, telling him the truth and asking him to take back any false statements he might have made in his panic. A letter was duly smuggled back to him, in which Cobham vowed that Walter had had nothing to do with the plot.

By English law a man is considered innocent until he has been proved guilty. But James considered himself free of the law, so, long before Walter came to trial, he was informed that his governorship of Jersey and his lieutenancy of Cornwall had been taken away and given to other men.

In September he was formally charged with "conspiring to deprive the King of his sovereignty, to alter the true religion, and to levy war." He was to have received ten thousand crowns from Spain for his services.

The plague was bad in London, so the trial was set for the seventeenth of November in Wolvesey Castle, at Winchester. Walter was sent down from London a week beforehand. It was all his escort could do to get him through the London mob alive; he was in danger every moment of being lynched.

It was incredible, he thought bitterly as they jeered and shouted for his blood, incredible what some fools would believe . . . and incredible how many fools there were.

"English justice had never been so degraded as at the trial of Raleigh."

That was the opinion of one of the judges, Justice Gawdy, given only a year or two later. It has been the general opinion ever since, and, needless to say, it was Walter's own opinion at the time.

He was fighting for his life. When he went into the dock and saw his judges, hand-picked by James to make sure they would give the right direction to the trial, he realized the full extent of his peril.

The jury had been changed the night before; it had been feared that the first jurymen chosen might possibly have found the prisoner not guilty. James was leaving nothing to chance.

The case began. Walter had never studied the law, but he knew enough to see when the judges twisted it or ignored it. He knew that he could not lawfully be convicted unless there were two witnesses against him; there was only one, Lord Cobham, but the judges ruled that one was enough. He knew that he was entitled to see that witness and cross-question him before the court, and he knew that Cobham would now declare him innocent, but the judges ruled that the witness might not be called.

Hour after hour the battle of words went on. Pale, calm, and alone, Walter fought like an expert fencer attacked by a gang. The Attorney-General, Sir Edward Coke, might whip himself into a frenzy; Walter remained unmoved. The Lord Chief Justice of England, Sir John Popham, might smugly announce, "We *know* the Law"; Walter, unruffled, merely pointed out another instance of the way it was being disregarded.

The Attorney-General, purposely addressing him with a contemptuous "thou," stormed, purple in the face, "Thou art the most vile and execrable traitor that ever lived!"

"You speak indiscreetly, barbarously, and uncivilly," Walter retorted in a quiet tone.

"I want words to express thy viperous treason!"

"I think you want words indeed, for you have said the same thing half a dozen times."

On they went, cut and thrust and parry all the time. Walter seemed fearless. When he had the chance to speak, he took the trial right out of the hands of judges, jury, and prosecutor alike. Listening to him, many of them had the uneasy feeling that *he* was trying *them*, instead of the other way around.

James had sent a personal representative to bring him a full report of the case. The man told him frankly afterward, "When I first saw Sir Walter Raleigh I felt as most people did—I'd have gone a hundred miles to see him hanged—"

"And now?" the King prompted eagerly.

"I'd go a thousand miles to save his life," said the man stoutly.

He was not the only one who had the courage to give James a fair impression of the proceedings. "No man has ever spoken so well before," vowed another, "and no man ever will in time to come."

In his main speech Walter riddled the case against

him until it was all holes. The idea of his plotting with Spain was obviously absurd.

"For me, at this time, to make myself a Robin Hood, a Wat Tyler, a Kett, or a Jack Cade!" he exclaimed scornfully. "I was not so mad! I knew the state of Spain well—his weakness, his poorness, his humbleness, at this time. I knew that six times we had repulsed his forces: thrice in Ireland, thrice at sea—once upon our coast, and twice upon his own. Thrice had I served against him myself at sea, wherein for my country's sake I have spent forty thousand marks of my own property."

There was quiet irony when he spoke of James, "an active king, who would be present at his own businesses." There were flashes of inspired phrasing when he referred to the newly dead Queen as a "lady whom Time had surprised."

But neither eloquence nor truth weighed with the court. Like a pack of hounds in full cry, they were set upon a kill.

They had no evidence against him but the first story Cobham had told, in his panic-stricken state, when he believed that Walter had betrayed him. They knew that if Cobham were put in the witness box, face to face with his old friend, he would unsay even that. They dared not risk it.

Walter staggered them by pulling out of his pocket the letter Cobham had sent him secretly. He handed it to Cecil, one of the special commissioners sitting to help the judges in the case. Cecil, who knew Cobham's writing, could not deny it was genuine.

"*I protest upon my soul,*" Cobham had written, "*and before God and His angels, I never had conference with you in any treason. . . . And, for anything I know, you are as innocent and as clear from any treasons against the King, as is any subject living.*"

Walter stood listening to the words which destroyed the last shred of evidence against him. If his judges had any respect for the law left in their minds, they could do only one thing: stop the case, tell the jury there was nothing to answer, and direct them to bring in a verdict of "Not guilty."

Was it too much to hope? It was. The Attorney-General leaped to his feet and declared that the letter had been extorted from Cobham by pressure; though how Walter from his own cell could exert pressure on another prisoner he did not try to explain.

It might have occurred to some people that, if any unfair pressure had been used on Cobham, it had been to make him accuse Walter in the first instance. So the Lord Chief Justice rose and explained that this could not possibly be so.

The jury went out to consider their verdict. They were back within a quarter of an hour. So quick a decision gave Walter a renewed flicker of hope. . . . Surely twelve men could not be persuaded to such a falsehood in so short a time? If they agreed so soon it must be that they saw through the whole farce and knew him innocent.

He heard the question boomed through the echoing hall, "How say you? Is the prisoner guilty or not guilty?"

Then the unbelievable answer, "Guilty, my lords."

Deathly pale, but composed, he listened to the Lord Chief Justice refer to him as a devil and warn him of Hell fire; and finally pronounce the frightful sentence of death passed in treason cases.

"I hope," said Walter in a firm, clear voice, "that the jury may never have to answer for this verdict."

Stepping up to the judges, he asked them one favor: that he might die honorably by the ax and not undergo the unspeakably savage tortures provided by the law. Cecil promised to do all he could: the little man had tears in his cold eyes. It should not be too difficult, it was often allowed now. . . . The mangling and hacking of bodies was no longer so popular.

Walter had left London the most hated man in England, but from Winchester his words took wings throughout the kingdom, and when he returned to his cell to wait for death he had become a hero.

His first thought now was for Bess and Wat. He had been stripped of all his offices and turned out of Durham House, but there was still Sherborne. A man executed for treason lost all his possessions to the King, and his sons were forever after tainted.

He must save his family all the sorrow he could. They must not be left without a penny in the world. Yet the only way to help them was by saving his own life.

So, for their sakes, he did what he would never have done for his own. He wrote letters, sickening in their humility, yet twice as sickening to himself as to anyone who read them, begging the King, Cecil, any councilor he could think of, to save him from the scaffold.

There were some who needed no such letters. The new Queen herself, Anne of Denmark, had been stirred by reports of the trial and won to a great admiration of the victim. She begged James to stop the execution. James coughed, slobbered, rolled his eyes, but said nothing.

Walter realized that he was doomed. Shivering in the December cold of his cell, he prepared himself to die.

It was then that he wrote "His Pilgrimage":

Give me my scallop shell of quiet,
My staff of faith to walk upon,
My scrip of joy, immortal diet,
My bottle of salvation,
My gown of glory, hope's true gage;
And thus I'll take my pilgrimage.
Blood must be my body's balmer;
No other balm will there be given;
Whilst my soul, like quiet palmer,
Traveleth toward the land of heaven;
Over the silver mountains,
Where spring the nectar fountains;
There will I kiss
The bowl of bliss;
And drink mine everlasting fill
Upon every milken hill.
My soul will be a-dry before;
But, after, it will thirst no more.

He was to die on the thirteenth of December. Four days before, in the midnight silence of his prison, he sat down by his candle to write to Bess:

"*You shall receive, dear wife, my last words in these my last lines. . . . I would not, with my last Will, present you with sorrows, dear Bess. Let them go to the grave with me, and be buried in the dust. . . .*

"*First, I send you all the thanks my heart can conceive, or my pen express, for your many troubles and cares taken for me. Pay it I never shall in this world. . . .*

"*I trust that my blood will quench their malice that desire my slaughter, and that they will not also seek to kill you and yours with extreme poverty. To what friend to direct you I know not, for all mine have left me in the true time of trial; and I plainly perceive that my death was determined from the first day. If you can live free from want, care for no more; for the rest is but vanity.*

"*Remember your poor child for his father's sake, that chose you and loved you in his happiest times. Get those letters (if it be possible) which I writ to the Lords, wherein I sued for my life, but God knows it was for you and yours that I desired it, but it is true that I disdain myself for begging it. And know it (dear wife) that your son is the child of a true man, who, in his own respect, despises Death in all his misshapen and ugly forms.*

"I cannot write much. God knows how hardly I stole this time, when all sleep. And it is time to separate my thoughts from the world. Beg my dead body, which living was denied you; and either lay it at Sherborne, if the land continue, or in Exeter church, by my father and mother. I can write no more. Time and Death call me away. . . ."

CHAPTER XIV

The Caged Eagle

JAMES LACKED many human qualities, but he had a certain wit, too cold and perverted to be regarded as a sense of humor, though he liked to think of it as such.

Cobham and the other condemned men were to die three days before Walter. On the morning after he had written his good-by to Bess he looked down from his narrow cell window upon the scaffold below. Just so, a year or two before, he had looked down from a window to see Essex die. Now the case was different: he was a spectator for the last time. Soon it would be his own turn.

He had reckoned without the King's idea of a joke.

The first prisoner, Sir Griffin Markham, was brought into the courtyard. A drizzle of rain was falling and it was dismal enough for dawn, though in fact it was ten o'clock. Sir Griffin prayed with the chaplain, made his farewell speech, and knelt before the block. At that moment there was a shouting from the back of the crowd and a man pushed his way forward with a letter, which he handed up to the Sheriff. Walter could not hear what was said, but he saw Sir Griffin led back into the castle. As the news passed through the crowd he caught the words "given another two hours to prepare for death."

Lord Grey, the next prisoner, came out. He mounted the scaffold firmly, but Walter noticed that he scraped aside the straw with his foot, and his friends murmured hopefully, because there was no blood on the planks. After a full half hour of prayers and farewell messages, Lord Grey was led back to his cell looking puzzled.

"The King says Cobham is to die first."

Straining his ears, Walter gathered that much information from the impatient spectators shifting their feet below his window. What did it mean?

They would soon know, for here came Cobham, cheerful of face, almost cocksure, not at all as Walter would have expected. Cobham he now knew for a coward, yet he wore a bolder front even than Lord Grey, who was none. Cobham made his entry like a popular actor, sure of his reception and (here was the point, Walter realized in a flash) knowing how the play would end.

The usual prayers were said. The rain fell softly from the leaden sky. The spectators huddled in their cloaks, and the executioner looked bored.

Prayers done, Cobham turned to the crowd to say his last words—and Walter knew, in an instant, that he was acting a part. He knew Cobham, had been his friend for years. . . . He wondered now how he had endured and even enjoyed the friendship of this creature . . . but he had never been good in his judgment of men. Of one thing, though, he could now be certain: Cobham would have behaved very differently if he had thought himself about to die. Cobham must have been promised his life, or he could not face the crowd so jauntily. But why?

He soon knew. Cobham's voice came clearly to him over the heads of the crowd:

"All and every part of my accusation of Sir Walter Raleigh was substantially true. . . ."

The liar! The hypocrite!

Walter clenched his hands. Cobham had changed his story yet again, bought his own miserable life by a false accusation of his friend! Would anyone believe it? Some people would believe anything.

Cobham was walking down from the scaffold, the

crowd was ebbing from the Castle yard, there would be no executions today.

Nor tomorrow, nor the day after. After long hours of suspense the cell door opened.

"Sir Walter, the King in his great mercy has spared your lives."

"You mean—a pardon?"

"No, the sentence of death stands, but it will not be carried out. You will be taken to London, and you will stay in the Tower during His Majesty's pleasure."

"I see."

He saw it all. After that trial James dared not send him to the block, dared not keep him in prison without fresh evidence—yet dared not set him free. So James had bought back what evidence he could from Cobham and hoped it would be enough to justify him in the eyes of England.

Having arranged that, James had enjoyed planning his comedy of the heads-that-didn't-come-off, and was only sorry that royal dignity stopped his being there to see. James loved his little joke.

"Bess!"

"Walter!" She ran across the room to meet him. "How are you?"

"Well enough, my dear." He gave her his chair and limped to another. The old wound ached in the damp atmosphere which rose from the Thames and seemed to creep through the thickest walls of the Tower. He said nothing of the paralysis which now gripped his left arm and side, or the bout of fever he had suffered while she had been down in Dorset.

"I've brought the clothes you asked for—they're in the coach, the servants will bring them up in a minute."

"And the books?"

"Yes, dear, I found everything on the list you gave me."

"Don't let anyone touch my chemicals. If I can get somewhere to work, I'll have them up here."

There was a moment's silence. Then she said, "Still no news, I suppose?"

He shook his head. "No. I've written letters to all sorts of people. So far, no result. I did think that after I'd had a few months here they'd have let me go home, even if it meant banishment from Court. They *can't* keep me here forever when the whole world knows I'm innocent."

Bess did not answer. She had an uneasy feeling that they could—and would. There were times when she felt she could carry on like this no longer, running between Dorset and London, working and praying and hoping against hope.

She changed the subject. "The King has promised me we shall not be put out of Sherborne."

"Good. How are things at home?"

"Not bad. Dear Laurence Kemys is looking after the estate. And, Walter . . ."

"Yes?"

"I thought it would be a good idea if I could find a house on Tower Hill—something quite cheap. Then I could be near you."

He looked straight at her. "Bess, do you imagine I am going to spend the rest of my life in prison?"

She bowed her head and began to cry, unwilling to answer his question.

Time passed. Winter after winter brought the gulls flashing upriver from the North Sea, March after March sent its gales to whine and moan around his quarters in the Bloody Tower, April after April pricked its daffodils and gillyflowers around the Lieutenant's Garden, where he was allowed to walk for exercise. Summer passed into autumn, autumn into winter again . . . still there was no release.

Bess had found her house just outside the gates, and visited him almost every day. Sometimes, when there was a well-disposed Lieutenant of the Tower, she was even allowed to stay inside with him. She had another baby in the year of the Gunpowder Plot, and they gave him the family name of Carew. Wat was growing up fast. By the time Carew was toddling unsteadily around the house, Wat had gone up to Corpus Christi, next door to Walter's own old college at Oxford.

It all took money, and sometimes she was worried to death. It was lucky she had a tiny income of her own. They had lost Sherborne in the end. James had decided to give it to one of his foppish young courtiers and the lawyers had conveniently discovered ten words missing from the original document conveying the estate to Walter.

Those ten words, never noticed at the time, meant that the estate had never legally been theirs. It was a mere slip of a clerk's pen, and a generous man would have overlooked it. But it was useless to look for generosity in James.

Bess fought for their home. She waylaid the King at Hampton Court and went down on her knees to him. He passed by without a word. She intercepted him again when he came back a little while after. He only rolled his eyes and shambled past, muttering, "I mun ha' the land for Kerr, I mun ha' it."

Later, to quiet his conscience, he promised her a lump sum of money in compensation–and remembered to pay her some of it.

To add insult to injury, Walter was charged board and lodging for his imprisonment in the Tower, which came to nearly six pounds a week. While he had Sherborne he could find enough. After that, Bess had to spend her private income to keep him as well as herself and the boys.

Often she was in despair, but she kept going, for Walter's sake and theirs. When her courage was at a low ebb she could always revive it by going to visit him.

He never lost heart completely. He annoyed the King, she knew, by refusing to behave like a guilty conspirator, a man dead in the eyes of the law and alive only by the King's mercy. Instead, Walter kept his head high, talking and behaving like a distinguished statesman and commander who was only temporarily–and quite unfairly–robbed of his liberty.

To back him loyally, as she always did, Bess used to order her coach (short though the distance was) and drive into the courtyard, as though she were visiting a great personage in his private mansion.

That used to annoy the authorities intensely.

They thought a prisoner's wife should have come on foot, meekly and shamefacedly knocking at the gates and begging as a favor to see the captive within.

He was not lonely. He had his own servants; they managed to make his rooms comfortable, and friends came to see him. Kemys, Dick Hakluyt, and Hariot were faithful. Even the Guiana Indians, whom he had brought back from the Orinoco years before, came to live on Tower Hill and visited him.

There were newer friends, too. Ben Jonson, whom he had known at the Mermaid Tavern gatherings, kept in touch with him and, when Wat left Oxford, agreed to act as his tutor and take him to France. Ben was an extraordinary fellow. His father had been a poor London bricklayer, but he had managed to attend Westminster School, and after that his own passion for study had done the rest.

"I never went to Oxford or Cambridge," he boasted, "but they both made me an honorary Master of Arts."

He was no meek, pale student, but a tall, bulky, blustering fellow, inclined to talk and drink too much, but so brilliant that you forgave him. He was quarrelsome and had been to prison for killing an actor in a duel. He would bear to the end of his days a branded T (for Tyburn) on his left thumb, and had narrowly escaped hanging.

Lately, though, he had risen in the world. His plays had made him the foremost dramatist after Will Shakespeare, and he was now writing masques, a form of entertainment far more popular with James and his Court, who preferred music, dancing, and general showmanship to straight plays.

As a tutor to the young, Ben was less successful. Bess arrived at the Tower one morning to find Walter knitting his brows over a letter from a friend in Paris.

"Oh, Walter, is there news from Wat?"

"News *of* him, the young villain."

"What's the matter? What's he been up to?"

"He got Ben dead drunk—you know what Ben is with liquor—laid him on a handcart, and had him pulled through the streets of Paris."

Bess let out a peal of laughter. "Oh, he *is* naughty!"

"Nothing to laugh at," Walter grumbled. "It's no way for a boy to treat his tutor."

Bess went on laughing all the same. "It's no good your looking so solemn," she said, wagging her finger, "I remember too many of the stories you've told me about the days when *you* were young. Wat's only taking after his father. Anyhow, I'd rather he played tricks like that than got drunk like Ben."

Walter could hardly disagree. . . .

Another occasional visitor was Francis Bacon, lawyer, scientist, and author—one of the most brilliant intellects in England. No visitor, but a fellow prisoner, was Lord Northumberland, the "wizard Earl," who had been in the old School of Night. The Earl had been sent to the Tower after the Gunpowder Plot and, like Walter, kept there indefinitely. With their books and learned visitors the pair of them were gradually turning the prison into a miniature university.

Of all who came, perhaps Walter's favorite was young Henry, the Prince of Wales.

Henry was utterly different from his father. He took after the Queen, who approved of the friendship and went on patiently trying to get Walter released.

Henry was in his teens. He loved tennis, riding, and swimming in the Thames. He had all the toughness and courage his father lacked, but was quiet and modest in his manners, never blustering or swearing to show his manhood, as most boys did.

"I don't know any game to be won or lost that's

worth an oath," he remarked once when beaten on the tennis court.

He knew that one day he must be King of England, but the masques and ceremonies of the palace bored him. He was happiest out of doors or sitting in Walter's room, discussing books or ships.

The sea was his passion. Walter was the last survivor of the great men who had fought the Armada, stormed Cadiz, and sailed the Spanish Main. He loved to hear of those voyages, to discuss Guiana and Virginia, and to learn the last detail about the design and building of a ship.

"I'd like to sail with you," he said wistfully, "and Wat, and Mr. Kemys. . . . Wouldn't it be wonderful?"

"I shall never sail again."

"Don't give up hope, Sir Walter."

"Some years ago," said Walter slowly, "when your uncle, the King of Denmark, was in London, he asked your father to let me go so that he could make me one of his own admirals." He laughed bitterly. "Have you ever heard of a prisoner before whose freedom was begged by a king, a queen, and a king's son—yet refused?"

Henry flushed. Tears of grief and anger stood in his eyes. "I know, Sir Walter . . . I am ashamed. A man like you! No one but my father would keep such a bird in a cage!"

"Never mind, it is not your fault. Look, now, I've finished the model ship I promised to make you. Now if only this design were adopted throughout the Navy . . ."

After that they were happy for an hour.

And still the time went by. Other men colonized Virginia and sailed eastward to India. The Mermaid Tavern was noisy with wit and good fellowship, the theaters were packed for Ben's *Alchemist* and Shakespeare's *Tempest* . . . and in Dorset the westerly breeze ran soft and warm over the green downs.

Meanwhile, within the narrow walls of the Tower, Walter lived on, his spirit unbroken, with no wider view of the outside world than he could get from the terrace where he walked for exercise. The Londoners knew him and pointed out the head and shoulders moving slowly along the battlements. He was a legend now, the man the King had not dared to kill. Children living in the houses around the Hill could not remember a time when Sir Walter had not walked that terrace.

Sometimes they missed him for days together. He was ill. The paralysis grew worse, all down his left arm and side. He had shivery, feverish bouts, a relic of the malaria he had caught in Guiana.

After a time he had been given the use of an old henhouse in the Lieutenant's Garden for his chemical experiments. Here he invented a new way of curing tobacco and of extracting fresh water from salt. One of his preparations, a cordial which contained quinine among other secret ingredients, was taken by the Queen during a serious illness. She gave it the credit for saving her life, but James either did not believe her or did not care enough about her life; he still refused to say the word which would let Walter go.

The damp rising from the river did him no good, and at last he managed to get a small room built onto his chemical laboratory, where he could live more healthily than in the Bloody Tower.

Here he wrote. It was no longer poetry. At first it was pamphlets on political matters. . . . Should we make friends with our old enemy, Spain? Should Prince Henry marry into the royal family there?

Cecil visited him to point out that he was a State prisoner now, not a statesman. He should be thankful to be alive at all. He should keep his mouth shut and his pen still, not meddle in the outside world where he had ceased to exist.

Walter was polite, but took no notice. He was an innocent man, he knew, wrongly imprisoned. That was bad enough. Why should he be silenced utterly?

He went on writing. He wrote of military matters and religion and naval architecture. He was the first man, not only in England but in the world, to write a whole book on ship design from the earliest ages to his own day.

Finally, encouraged by Prince Henry, he began to write *The History of the World.*

It was a staggering task. No one before had even considered it. But it was not the first time Walter had tried to do something entirely new. He began at the Creation, as described in the Bible, and wrote tirelessly. Friends helped him collect his facts. He knew no Hebrew, but others did. Ben Jonson, a better classical scholar than himself, helped with the account of Rome's struggle against Carthage.

The years passed.

Cecil died. He ended as an Earl, his death more popular than anything else he did. Walter mourned him no more than anyone did. Cecil had been a false friend. Visitors told him the verses that were going about the town:

The devil now hath fetched the ape
Of crooked manners, crooked shape . . .

and (what seemed especially to fit his own experience of the man):

Here lieth Robin Crookback, unjustly reckoned
A Richard the Third, he was Judas the Second.

A few months later Prince Henry burst in, his face shining with good news.

"Sir Walter! I've something wonderful to tell you."

Walter laid down his pen and smiled. Henry was one of the very few who could interrupt him without his minding.

"Well?"

"Father's promised me a Christmas present—at least, it took a bit of dragging out of him, but he *has* promised it, and he won't dare to change his mind."

Walter looked at the hefty eighteen-year-old, glowing from his ride, and remembered the timid, shifty King. No, he could scarcely imagine James standing up to his son now he was grown into such a man.

"And what is this wonderful Christmas present?"

"Your freedom!"

For a moment Walter could find no words. For nine years he had been a prisoner. To be free again would take some getting used to.

"Just a few months longer," Henry rushed on excitedly, "then at Christmas you'll be out of all this! And I've a gift for you myself."

"I–I don't know what else . . . what *more* . . . I could be given."

The Prince grinned affectionately. "What about–Sherborne?"

"*Sherborne!*"

"I got it from Father some time ago. Bullied him, told him it was too fine a place to give away outside the royal family. . . . In the end he gave it to me. And I've been keeping it for you. As soon as you're free I shall have much pleasure in handing it back to you–the rightful owner."

For a month or two Walter and Bess lived in a world of rosy hopes. Then fell perhaps the cruelest blow of all.

Prince Henry was taken ill. After a hearty supper of fruit he had gone swimming in the Thames at Richmond. It was late October, a chilly season for an evening bathe, but Henry prided himself on his toughness.

In a few days he was desperately ill with typhoid fever.

The Queen wanted to give him Walter's cordial, which had saved her own life, but neither the doctors nor the Council would hear of it.

Medicine from a convicted traitor—for the Prince of Wales? What if Raleigh sent poison instead?

For nearly a fortnight they battled at the bedside. Henry was past speech and gradually sinking. At last his mother won her way and a messenger hurried off to the Tower. He came back promptly, the Queen knelt and pressed the cup to her son's mouth. Half conscious, he swallowed most of the drink.

They waited anxiously. After an age there was a slight improvement. His eyelids flickered, he spoke. . . .

The Queen turned triumphantly to the doctors. "You see? It works!"

But it had come too late. After that short rally the Prince sank steadily and died without speaking again.

With his life passed Walter's hope of freedom and England's hope of peace in years to come. Prince Charles was henceforth heir to the throne, a very different boy; and now the path of history lay open to the battles of Marston Moor and Naseby.

Walter had delayed publishing the first part of *The History of the World* to please Prince Henry, who had asked him to fill out certain chapters with extra detail.

Now at last it was ready, though the boy had not lived to see it in print. It was a tremendous work, written in noble, musical prose, but on the whole simpler and more natural than the style generally in fashion. It did not bring the story further than ancient Rome, yet it covered 1,354 large folio pages and contained roughly one million words. Though it dealt with such far-off events, it was made vivid by examples and comparisons from modern times, many of them firsthand experiences Walter had known during his varied life.

The book was an immediate success. The King tried to ban it. He found Walter "too saucy" in criticizing monarchs of the past, and was afraid people might apply the criticisms to himself.

But the *History* was far too popular a book to be killed. The best he could do, at the finish, was to rob Walter of the credit for writing it. Orders were given that the title page, carrying his name and portrait, should be removed from all copies sold.

Three editions were sold within as many years, and it was translated into several foreign languages.

But Walter had not the heart to go on with the other volumes he had planned. It had been written to please the Prince, and Henry was dead. Why, too, should he be denied the credit for what he wrote?

"If I am not considered worthy to be of the world," he said when he heard the King's order about the title page, "then the world is not worthy of my works."

It seemed that his fortune had reached its bottom level. All hope was dead.

Then the unbelievable thing happened. The King unlocked the prison door.

CHAPTER XV

Guiana Gold

JAMES WANTED MONEY. He had tried every way he could think of. He had sold knighthoods for cash; he had invented the new title of baronet, and that, too, was for sale; if you paid enough you could buy a peerage.

That idea was now worked out. Decent men, seeing the scoundrels who now had titles to their names, preferred to remain without. There seemed more dignity in a plain "Esquire."

The last thing he wanted to do was to ask help from Parliament. Elizabeth had always got on very well with her Parliament—they understood each other and knew that neither could get on alone. James would have dismissed Parliament forever if only he could have been sure of enough money from other sources.

But how? Where?

What about Sir Walter Raleigh's Guiana? Had

not his lieutenant, Kemys, discovered evidence of a rich gold mine at Mount Aio, a few miles from where the Caroni joined the Orinoco?

Bribed with the last few hundred pounds that Walter could raise, the King's favorites whispered the suggestion into the royal ear.

Why not let Sir Walter out of the Tower—on one condition: that he lead an expedition to the gold mine and bring back such a shipload of treasure that the King could snap his fingers at money difficulties for years to come?

James wagged his head and wondered, his eyes gleaming but his heart fearful. What would the Spaniards say? He must keep friends with Spain. . . .

There had been no Spaniards in that region when Sir Walter was last there, his favorites assured him. That side of the river had been no man's land. In fact, Sir Walter had claimed it for the Queen of England.

James muttered and fiddled with uneasy hands. He wanted the gold, but he wanted Spanish friendship. Was it possible to have both?

It was worth trying. If Raleigh could bring the gold without trouble, excellent. If the Spaniards made a fuss he could always say that Raleigh had disobeyed orders. The Spaniards could have Raleigh's head—they could cut it off themselves in Madrid if they liked. That should please them.

"Heads I win: tails you lose." James had enough sporting spirit to appreciate that kind of a gamble. He gave orders for Walter's release.

It was a March day when Walter, having packed his books and papers, his globes and mathematical instruments and chemical apparatus, drove out of the Tower to Bess's house on the Hill nearby.

He had entered that gate as a middle-aged man, just turned fifty. He came out gray-haired and old, verging on his middle sixties.

The London he had left had been still the London of the old Queen; the London he found was Stuart. New buildings, new names on the playbills, new faces. . . . When he walked into the "Mermaid" there were few he remembered, though all knew him and fell silent when he first entered, a gaunt, silver-bearded ghost from an earlier time.

Yes, he had outlived most of them. Marlowe, Spenser, Essex, Cecil . . . Within a few weeks he heard that even the young man who had once mocked him in *Love's Labor Lost*—even Will Shakespeare had died in his Warwickshire retirement.

Retirement? Walter smiled bitterly. He had had his fill of retirement—twelve and a half years in the Tower! If things had happened differently this *would* have been the time to speak of retirement, of last sunny years spent with Bess at Sherborne, with voyages and adventures left to Wat and Carew.

But no. Action was the price of his liberty. He must nerve his old body for this last adventure.

Preparations took a long time. Men of common sense knew it was a desperate enterprise and were in no haste to volunteer. Walter had no power to conscript men. He had to gather his crews from the scum of the water-front taverns. Funds were as short as usual.

Kemys was coming, of course. Where Walter went he went. Anyhow, it was he who had heard of the mine on his second trip to Guiana, when Walter was occupied with Cadiz.

Young Wat was sailing, too. It was high time, Walter felt, that the boy had a father's discipline. He had been in trouble only the year before—a little matter of a duel—and had been forced to slip out of the country for a while. He was a good enough lad, but too hotheaded.

"We're going out to dinner tonight," Walter told him one morning after his release. "You're invited, but I'm almost ashamed to take you on an important occasion like this—your manners are so bad."

Wat promised faithfully to be good. All went well until the middle of dinner. Wat sat next to his father, and kept mum. At last, however, he could no longer control the imp inside him, and he came out with the wrong remark.

Walter turned on his stool and gave him a resounding box on the ear. The boy swayed in his place, his eyes blazing. For a moment the party thought he was going to return his father's blow. Even Wat did not dare to do that, but his devil must out somehow.

With a laugh he turned and boxed the ear of the harmless guest sitting on his other side.

"Let it go around the table!" he shouted wickedly. "It will come back to Father at the end!"

Yes, thought Walter grimly, it was high time the boy had a taste of discipline.

His preparations went forward month by month. The King signed his commission for the voyage. "That's as good as a pardon," Francis Bacon assured him. "Obviously, if you were still considered guilty of treason, you could not receive such a commission."

As Bacon was Lord Keeper of the Seal, his opinion on a matter of law was to be trusted. They were walking with young Carew in the gardens of Gray's Inn at the time.

"What will you do," asked Bacon, "if—after all this expense—you don't find your gold mine?"

"Oh," said Walter jokingly, "then we'll look for the treasure convoy from Mexico."

"But then you'll be pirates!" cried the horrified lawyer.

Walter's eyes twinkled. He remembered times past, when the Queen of England had been pleased to overlook irregular behavior, provided it happened far enough away and the loot was large enough. Only petty thieves were punished.

"Oh, no," he assured his companion, "who ever heard of men's being pirates for millions?"

He might have added that any man who could have brought James such wealth would soon have been a peer, not a pirate. But he also knew that James was far too scared of Spain for such an idea to be considered seriously.

Altogether a year passed before the expedition was ready to start. Bess and Carew went down to Plymouth to see them off. It warmed her heart to see the welcome Plymouth gave to Walter. Whatever had befallen him elsewhere, he remained the hero of his own West Country. The city gave him a banquet and paid a drummer to beat through the streets, gathering all his men to the tables. Walter looked around with tears in his eyes. It was as though twenty years had rolled back and the good old days had come again.

There, in the Sound, lay the little fleet he had brought around from Dover. His flagship, the *Destiny*, of four hundred and forty tons; the *Star*, the *Encounter*, the *John and Francis*, the *Flying Joan* . . . in all, seven warships and three pinnaces, with a total of several hundred men—sailors, soldiers, gentlemen adventurers, and miners.

Money difficulties dogged them to the last moment. Several of the captains could not sail because their stores were not paid for. Walter sold his family plate to meet one bill; he borrowed two hundred pounds from friends to settle another; and a third, a grocery account, was taken over by Bess herself.

At last, by the second week in June, all was ready. Their kit was on board. Walter's chest of books, without which he never sailed, was in his cabin, together with his carved silver pipe and plenty of tobacco. The last farewells were said.

"Don't worry about the boy," he told Bess, "I'll look after him."

"Look after *yourself*," she answered, "you're the one to worry about."

He kissed her and handed her ashore. The anchor chains clanked, the men panted and sang as they circled the capstan.

Spreading her white wings, the *Destiny* glided out of the Sound and sought the West.

They had bad weather at first. One storm drove them back to Plymouth, another to Falmouth, and a third to Kinsale. "At least we are making progress," said one gentleman bitterly as they saw Ireland fade behind them at last, two months after leaving Devon.

They put into the Canary Islands. Three men were murdered ashore. Walter sent a message to the local governor, who had defied him to do his worst, "If I were not unwilling to offend my own King, I would have pulled you and your people out of the town by your ears!"

With that he sailed away, doing no harm. But fresh water he must have, for sick men on board, so he put into the last of the islands, Gomera. His landing party was fired on, and he sent a few shots in answer. After that, cordial relations were established.

It turned out that this governor's wife was half English. Walter sent her half a dozen fine-quality kerchiefs and as many pairs of gloves. Delighted, she returned the compliment with baskets of grapes, oranges, lemons, pomegranates, and figs, which he gave to his sick men, and four great sugar loaves.

More gifts were exchanged while his ships lay watering. He sent her a picture, a ruff, rose water and perfumes; she answered with two dozen plump chickens and other provisions equally welcome after so many days at sea.

The lady's fruit saved his life, as he told Bess in a letter afterward. Bad weather struck them again after the Canaries; then they were becalmed in tropical heat while fever ran through the ships. Over forty men died in the *Destiny* alone. Walter himself was desperately ill for a fortnight, and was unable to swallow proper food for a whole month. His friends thought he was dying, but his will was like steel, and he lived.

So they came to Guiana at long last, their numbers and their stores much diminished. Morale had never been high; only Walter's firm but sensible discipline could keep such men together. When they reached the mouth of the Orinoco they were met by rumors which depressed them still more.

The Spaniards were expecting them. Full details of the expedition—its strength, its plans, its timetable—had been given by James to the Spanish Ambassador in London, Count Gondomar, who had lost no time in passing them on to Madrid. A Spanish fleet might appear at any moment to attack them.

It was clear that, as the months had passed, James's nerve had gone completely. He wanted the gold mine, but only if Spain did not claim the country; and, to prove to Spain that he was doing nothing behind her back, he had told Gondomar every detail.

James wanted to eat his cake and have it—to make omelets without breaking eggs.

There were many who wanted to give up the whole venture and sail away while there was time. Walter would not hear of it.

He was still weak in body, but his will remained. He had himself carried ashore, still taking little but lemon juice, and camped by the river mouth. Friendly Indians crowded in from the surrounding villages. There were some who had spent years in London and had known him in the Tower. Others, who had not stirred from Guiana, remembered him from his visit twenty-two years before. They brought piles of fresh provisions and begged to serve him in any way.

Meanwhile time pressed, the gold mine lay far up-river, and the Spaniards might interfere at any time. He was forced to admit that he was still unfit to make such a journey himself—and none of the men would agree to make it unless he promised to remain with the fleet at the river mouth and cover their retreat.

Walter, they knew, would not desert them. No matter how many Spanish vessels appeared, he would never cut and run, leaving them to their fate.

"Don't fear," he assured them, "I'll stay here and take you off again, whatever happens."

They knew that was true.

So Kemys took charge of the river party, and young Wat accompanied him. Their orders were clear: they must be as careful to avoid trouble with the Spaniards as Walter himself had been when they called at the Canary Islands. Apart from that, they were to find the mine, if possible, and bring back all the gold they could.

Weeks passed without news, but also (to Walter's relief) without any sign of Spanish vessels off the coast. He grew stronger. As the anchorage was unsuitable, he cruised about the neighborhood, collecting medicinal plants and other specimens which caught his interest.

Christmas passed. Kemys had been gone more than a month, though he had taken provisions only for that time. Surely nothing had gone wrong? Kemys was a good man, he knew the country, the natives were friendly. . . .

Late in January he heard of an alarming rumor among the Indians: there had been a battle between the Spaniards and the English upriver. In mid-February he received definite news in a letter from Kemys, which had taken five weeks to arrive.

He groaned when he read the letter, and covered his eyes. The news could not have been worse.

The party had been ambushed by Spaniards near a settlement named San Thomé. . . . ("What were they doing near San Thomé," he muttered to himself, "when I told them at all costs to avoid the Spaniards?")

The Englishmen, scratch lot as they were, had wavered. Young Wat had rallied them, behaving like a hero. Then, with his usual hotheadedness, he had led them pell-mell in a counterattack against the settlement and died there in the moment of victory.

It was a whole day before he could face the task of writing to Bess. Then he set his teeth and wrote:

"I was loth to write, because I knew not how to comfort you; and God knows, I never knew what sorrow meant until now. All that I can say to you is, that you must obey the will and providence of God. Comfort your heart, dearest Bess, I shall sorrow for us both. My brains are broken and it is a torment for me to write. . . ."

Kemys came back empty-handed. They had never reached the mine. There was a furious interview in Walter's cabin. Distracted by illness and grief, Walter attacked his old friend with bitter words that afterward he would gladly have unsaid. Kemys had disobeyed orders, he had wrecked everything, he had left Wat's body within three miles of the mine, yet he had not even reached his objective.

"Very well, sir," said Kemys with quiet dignity, "I know then what course to take."

He went to his own cabin. A few minutes later Walter heard a shot. Anxiously he called a boy. "Go to Captain Kemys and see if he is all right."

The boy was back in a moment. "The captain's all right, sir—at least, he's lying down on his bunk and he doesn't sound ever so well. But he said not to be alarmed by the pistol–he fired it through the porthole to clear the barrel, it had been loaded a long time."

"I see."

But when they went to find Kemys an hour later he was dead. The bullet wound had not been fatal, so he had driven a knife into his heart.

CHAPTER XVI

The Fall of a Star

WHAT WAS TO BE DONE NOW?

At first Walter decided to go upcountry himself; he would bring back the gold he had promised the King or he would lay his bones beside those of his son.

Not a man would go with him. He then considered withdrawing to the new English colony in Virginia to refit and try again. They would not agree to that. The expedition was beginning to melt away.

It was dangerous to go home empty-handed. Common sense suggested: stay overseas, you have your own ship, you are Raleigh and you will always find men to serve under you . . . but not on wild-goose chases up the Orinoco. No, keep to the open sea, take service with the King of France, or even turn pirate. Why go back and surrender yourself to James?

But he had given his word of honor to return.

And there was still Bess and the other boy. . . . He set course for Plymouth and sailed for home. Just a year after the fleet had left the Sound, the *Destiny* returned alone.

Bess hurried to meet him. There was trouble brewing, and she was determined to be at his side. News of the San Thomé fight had already reached London, and the Spanish Ambassador was breathing fire and slaughter.

Walter told her not to worry. Though the fight had been so tragic for them as a family, it was a small affair as between nations; much worse incidents had been overlooked before. The Spaniards had attacked first anyhow, and he himself had been hundreds of miles from the spot. He had failed to bring gold—if James wanted the gold he must be willing to fight Spain for it—but at least the *Destiny* had brought back a valuable cargo.

"Everything will be all right," he assured her, patting her hand.

They had started for London together when they met Sir Lewis Stukeley with orders to arrest him. He had no warrant, but Walter did not argue the point. He continued the journey under Stukeley's escort, with a French doctor, Manourie, in the party, who seemed friendly.

They passed Sherborne. There, on the mound, stood the castle that had been his. There, in all their June glory, stood the trees he had planted. That smoke was climbing from the chimneys of the house he had built for Bess. . . .

"All this was mine," he told the Frenchman with a sigh, "but it was taken from me unjustly."

Manourie showed great sympathy. That gave Walter an idea.

They were now approaching Salisbury. So, from another direction, was the King. If only he could invent an excuse for delaying in the town until James arrived, he might be able to get a personal interview with him and explain everything.

He took the doctor aside. Could he make him up some medicines? He wanted to clear his system of the poisons collected during his long illness. Manourie promised to give him something at Salisbury.

When they reached the inn Walter put his plan into practice. He shammed dizziness, fell, and had to be carried to bed. The next day, when it was time to move on, they found him rolling naked on the floor as if in agony. Manourie came to attend him and provided the medicine he had asked for, which made him violently sick.

This sort of play acting was too painful and exhausting to keep up for long. Yet time he must have. If he could not see the King (and there seemed less chance of that now) he must gain time to write out a full defense of all he had done on the expedition. Bess, too, who had gone ahead to London, must have a day or two to rally friends to his support. If he arrived in London now, his enemies might whip off his head before there was a chance to put his case to the King.

Accordingly he changed his line, got some skin irritant from Manourie, and smeared it over his body to produce angry-looking blotches. Three doctors were called in to see him. They were completely fooled and signed a certificate that he was far too ill to be moved. It might be leprosy.

The patient meanwhile was refusing food. Actually the helpful Frenchman had smuggled in a leg of mutton and three loaves from another inn, the White Hart. Alone in his room after midnight, when all were asleep, Walter sat up furiously writing out his defense and eating cold mutton and bread, the crumbs of which he was careful to dispose of before dawn.

The King sent word that he would not see Walter; the prisoner was to be taken on to London, but he might live for the present (under due watch) in his own house.

It was astonishing how quickly and completely the patient then recovered.

Bess was awaiting him at home in Broad Street. She knew how great his danger was, however much he tried to reassure her. He must think of himself now, she insisted, not of her or Carew. He had kept his word in returning to England. He had a perfect right to escape now if he could.

There were plenty who wanted him to escape. The French government offered to receive him as an honored guest if he cared to cross the Channel until the storm blew over.

England just now was sharply divided into those who were pro-Spanish and those who were anti-Spanish. The latter included the Queen. Since to be anti-Spanish meant to be pro-French, she was among those who would gladly have seen Walter safe in Paris.

When Stukeley himself offered to help him get away—Stukeley was, after all, a relative, and Walter had previously found that relatives made friendly jailers—he saw that he would be a fool to wait longer.

"I can fix everything," Stukeley assured him. "There's a ship at Tilbury that will take you across.

I'll have a boat waiting on the Thames tonight. Send your servants by different routes; go by yourself, so that no suspicions are aroused. I'll meet you there."

Walter made his preparations during that day. He must travel light. His clothes and a few treasured books went separately. In his pockets he carried fifty pounds in gold, a diamond ring Elizabeth had given him, and a few other personal possessions he specially valued—a jeweled miniature containing a portrait of Bess, his naval officer's whistle, gold and set with small diamonds, and an Indian idol he had brought as a souvenir from Guiana.

Darkness fell. He had supper, talked with Bess, and then laughingly adjusted a false beard. Bess did not feel like laughing. They said good-by, and he slipped out into the summer night.

Stukeley and the others were waiting at the wharf. They got in and pushed off. As they started downriver, the ebb tide and current helping them, another craft nosed out of the shadows behind them. Ten minutes later it was still astern.

"Whose boat is that?" Walter demanded suddenly.

"Sh! If you're going to take fright at every boat we see on the river . . ."

Take fright! Walter swallowed his annoyance and

made no retort. Stukeley was a good fellow to take risks for him like this. But he still did not like that second boat behind them.

Their own watermen were getting suspicious, too. They had not been told the meaning of this midnight journey. The money was all right, of course, but it was not enough to make up for a stretch in prison. They stopped rowing and began to ask awkward questions. The second boat also stopped.

By the time the discussion with the boatmen was settled, the tide had turned and was running strongly against them. Walter realized that it was now impossible to make Tilbury. He had put himself in a difficult and dangerous position and must make the best of it. His only hope was to turn back, land at Greenwich, and hurry home before daylight. It might not be discovered that he had ever tried to escape.

No such luck. The second boat turned after them and slid into the bank at Greenwich as they did.

"I arrest you in the King's name!"

It was Stukeley who spoke the fatal words. He handed over his prisoner to the men in the other craft. Walter was kept that night in Greenwich and taken over the river to the Tower next day.

Meanwhile, Sir Lewis Stukeley reported how, in accordance with instructions, he had allowed Sir

Walter Raleigh to plan an escape and had then arrested him in the act. At much the same time the French doctor was writing an account for the government of Walter's wickedness in shamming sick.

James was in a difficulty. For what reason could he put Walter to death?

His advisers warned him that Walter had done nothing really, either on the voyage or since coming back, for which he could be heavily punished.

Since he could not be executed for fighting the Spaniards, could he not be executed for plotting *with* them? After all, he had been sentenced on that charge fifteen years ago, and had never been properly pardoned.

That, on the whole, seemed the best line to take. To say that the execution of 1603 had been merely postponed, and would now in 1618 be carried out.

People would think it strange, of course, that a man's life should be taken, to please Spain, on a charge of plotting with Spain. And that a man should have been allowed, in the meantime, to command a fleet with the King's commission, *unless* he were considered clear of the old charge.

What people thought, however, had never been of much interest to James. He was more interested in his alliance with Spain and the cash he would gain by it. Walter's life was just an item in the transaction.

James would not risk another public trial. He remembered too well what had happened at Winchester, when Walter had been in the depths of his unpopularity. If he were allowed to put his case to the world now he might raise such a storm that even a king would have to bend before it. The inquiry was held in private.

Even so, Walter fought back. When his judges taxed him with the recent doings at San Thomé, he reminded them of what earlier Englishmen had suffered from the Spaniards without James raising a word of protest to their government.

"If it were lawful," he persisted, "for the Spanish to murder twenty-six Englishmen, tying them back to back and then cutting their throats—when they had traded with them for a whole month and come ashore without so much as a sword among them—and if it is not lawful now for His Majesty's subjects, being forced by them, to repel force by force, then we may justly say, 'Oh, miserable English!' "

But his judges did not dare to be impressed. They had their orders. On a morning late in October he was roused early and told to dress. He was to go before the King's Bench and hear their decision.

He was unwell. His malaria was back, and he had fits of shivering from time to time. Normally he would have spent a long time combing his hair, which he wore long and curly, though it was now almost white. Today he felt too ill to trouble with his appearance.

An old servant, Peter, offered to help. "No," he said wearily, "I'll know first who's to have my head —if it's the executioner, I'll not bother." Then he smiled with a flash of his old humor. "Peter, do you know of any plaster to set a man's head on again when it's off?"

He went before his judges once more. The Attorney-General rose and asked that the sentence passed so many years before should now at last be carried out. His tone was grave and courteous, very different from the insults that other Attorney-General had shrieked in the Winchester trial.

"Sir Walter Raleigh," he said, "has been a statesman . . . a star at which the world has gazed. But stars may fall, nay, they must fall, when they trouble the sphere wherein they abide."

The Lord Chief Justice announced that the execution should take place. James paid no heed to any of the appeals for mercy which had poured in from many quarters. There was one in a neat, schoolboyish hand from thirteen-year-old Carew.

The warrant was ready. James signed it. Enough time had been wasted. Raleigh should die the very next morning, Lord Mayor's Day. With any luck he would attract a smaller crowd: people would be watching the other show.

Walter knew otherwise. As they led him from the court he saw an old friend, Sir Hugh Beeson.

"Tomorrow morning," said Walter quietly, answering the question in his eye, "here in Old Palace Yard. Will you do me the honor of being there?" His voice was as steady as if he had been asking Sir Hugh to dinner.

"Yes–if you wish it."

"Come early then and make sure of a good place." Walter's smile flickered as he moved away between his guards. "For my part, I am sure of one."

It was not worth taking him back to the Tower. He spent that last night in the Old Gatehouse of what had once been Saint Peter's Monastery, close to the spot where already the workmen were beginning to hammer up the scaffold.

Bess came to see him for the last time. His friends

had already been to visit him throughout the evening. He found himself comforting them instead of accepting the comfort they tried to bring. He remembered it had been so with Socrates on that last night in Athens two thousand years before. He, too, must meet his end with the same courage and good humor as the old Greek philosopher had shown.

But it was hard when Bess came, weeping and brokenhearted. . . .

He must talk of practical things. Carew's education: he must go to Oxford, of course, like his father and brother. Perhaps it would be a good plan to send him to Wadham, the newly founded college for West Countrymen. . . .

Another thing: suppose the King forbade his making a speech tomorrow, his last chance of clearing his name and honor in the eyes of the world. As Hamlet said in the play:

> *Thou liv'st: report me and my cause aright*
> *To the unsatisfied.*

So she must remember all the facts correctly, all the proofs of his innocence. She nodded, sobbing, and took the papers he handed to her.

It struck twelve. She must go. Her brother Nicholas was at the door to take her home. As they embraced for the last time, she stammered amid her tears that she had been promised his body for honorable burial.

"It's well, dear Bess," he said, smiling down into her face, "that you should be allowed to dispose of my dead body, which you could not always when it was alive."

The door clanged. He was alone with the silence of the night.

He had never wasted time in sleep, and he would not squander his last hours. For a long time his pen scratched over the paper. He had given Bess a full written account of what he meant to say if given the chance. He must make a few speaker's notes, so that nothing important slipped his memory. There were also one or two matters of private business to deal with.

These done, he opened his Bible. But, after a time, his memory wandered to some lines he had written at the end of a love poem long years before. How easily they could be adapted to his present mood! All that was needed was a slight alteration in one line, and a new couplet to round it off.

Taking up his pen again he wrote in his Bible:

Sir Walter Raleigh

Even such is Time, that takes in trust
Our youth, our joys, our all we have,
And pays us but with earth and dust;
Who in the dark and silent grave,
When we have wandered all our ways,
Shuts up the story of our days;
But from this earth, this grave, this dust,
My God shall raise me up, I trust.

Dawn was near. Cocks crowed from the farms over toward Chelsea and Kensington. The chaplain arrived and gave him Holy Communion. He dressed carefully but quietly, mainly in black, with gray silk stockings. He made a good breakfast and smoked his carved silver pipe for the last time. His one worry was his malaria. If a shivering fit seized him, people might imagine he was afraid.

The Sheriffs arrived. It was time to go. He put on a small lace cap under his hat, for the autumn air struck chilly, and went with them.

The King had miscalculated again: the crowds had not flocked to the City for the Lord Mayor's show, they were at Westminster to see the fall of a star. It was all the Sheriffs could do to push their way to the foot of the scaffold. They, and Walter, were breathless by the time they arrived.

"A glass of sherry, Sir Walter?"

"Thank you." He accepted it gravely, this stirrup cup offered before the last and greatest journey of all.

"I hope you find it to your taste?"

He smiled. "As the fellow said when he drank at Saint Giles's bowl on his way to Tyburn, 'It's a good drink, if only a man might tarry by it.' "

As he sipped it he noticed an old man in the crowd, his bald head uncovered. "What have *you* come out for on such a raw morning?" he called pleasantly. "Anything you want?"

"Nothing, sir! Only to see you, sir, and pray God for your soul."

"Thank you. I'm afraid this is the only return I can make." Walter removed his lace cap and tossed it over. "Put that on—you have more need of it now than I."

He handed back his empty wineglass. "There's a brazier, Sir Walter," one of the Sheriffs murmured, "if you'd care to warm your hands?"

"No, thank you, it might bring on my shivering fit again."

He mounted the scaffold, took off his hat and looked around. Below was a sea of faces, with many gentlemen mounted in order to see. In every house around Palace Yard the open windows were filled with ladies of noble family. The balconies were crowded with lords.

His voice was weak, as it had been for some years. He strained to make his words heard, then paused as he saw the lords coming down. An avenue was made through the human mass below, and they climbed up to shake hands with him, remaining on the scaffold until his speech was done.

Point by point he dealt with the case against him and answered them. Finally he asked for them all to join with him in prayer.

"I have been a seafaring man," he said, "a soldier, and a courtier; and in the temptations of the least of these there is enough to overthrow a good mind and a good man. I die in the faith professed by the Church of England and hope for salvation. So I take my leave of you all, making my peace with God. I have a long journey to take, and must bid the company farewell."

The scaffold was cleared. He took off his doublet and gown. The executioner spread his own cloak in front of the block for him to kneel on and came forward to ask Walter's forgiveness for what he now had to do.

"Of course. Gladly. May I feel the ax?" He ran

his finger along the edge and smiled. "This is a sharp medicine to cure all my diseases."

"Will you be blindfolded, sir?"

"No, no. Do you think I fear the shadow of the ax, when I don't fear the ax itself?"

He knelt.

"Wouldn't you wish to face the east, sir?"

"What does it matter which way the head lies if the heart is right? When I stretch out my hands, strike."

For a few moments he prayed. Then he gave the signal. Nothing happened.

"What do you fear?" he exclaimed impatiently. "Strike, man, strike!"

The ax fell. A deep groan went up from the crowd, but the body never stirred. There was a second blow. The executioner held up the head without a word. There was no man present who would have cared to speak the usual formula: Behold the head of a traitor.

It was left to an unknown voice, crying out from the midst of the crowd, to speak the thought of them all:

"We haven't another such head to be cut off!"

AUTHOR'S NOTE

Most people skip prefaces, so I put this at the end of the story, when some readers may want to ask questions.

What happened to Bess? She lived to the ripe old age of eighty-two. And Carew had an honourable career—he was an M.P. with Cromwell and refused a knighthood from Charles the Second.

Is this book true? Yes. How do we *know*? Because there are heaps and heaps of records—not only books written at the time, but diaries, letters, account books, law-court proceedings, oil paintings, Secret Service reports, and lots more. We really do know what Walter had in his pockets that night he was arrested at Greenwich, how much he was paid as an infantry captain in Ireland, and what he shouted to Essex from his boat at Cadiz.

We do not know the exact words of *all* his conversations—obviously, for instance, with Bess—or just what he was thinking at any given moment. One has to guess a little there, to bridge the gaps. But nothing important has been invented. The biggest bit of invention is this: how did he get *all* his ninety men into Lord Roche's castle? We know he did, "by a cunning stratagem," but no man alive knows what it was. So I had to guess or leave the story out entirely, which would have been a pity.

Finally, one or two curious points: what Walter called Guiana is now Venezuela, and his Virginia is now North Carolina. It is very likely that he never brought the potato from America; and, great seafarer though he was, a friend declared that Walter so disliked boats he would walk a long way around over London Bridge rather than cross to South London direct from his private landing stage. And, believe it or not, there are seventy-four different ways of spelling his surname, of which he used three himself at various times, not one of the three being Raleigh.

G. T.